"The family stories told in *Tal*[illegible] childhood and the many evenings I spent at my grandfather's knee begging for one more family story of hard work, struggle, and living a simple, Christian life with kindness and generosity for those in need. These stories will resonate with you and leave you with a sense of appreciation and nostalgia."

~ Krista L. Newkirk

President, Converse College

"The eight women so vividly described by Sheila Ingle knew hardship, but found ways to make a home, earn a living, encourage education, teach values and manners, and most of all instill a sense of self worth and pride in honest work. As I read, I could taste the cornbread and molasses, smell the clean clothes billowing on the clothes line, envision the cherished quilted and tatted keepsakes, and hear the beautiful hymns. Most of all, I could see a ninth woman who was a single mother who worked in the local mill for fifty-two years, took her daughters to church, taught them to value education, good manners and hard work. For I am a daughter of the ninth woman and a 'daughter' of Sheila Ingle's pioneering women and I enjoyed immensely visiting with my kin!"

~ Dr. Ann Bowles

Administrator at Spartanburg Methodist College,
formerly Textile Industrial Institute

"Like her characters who preserved peaches and beans in the summer to be enjoyed in the winter, Sheila Ingle has preserved the stories of her husband's family to be enjoyed now that they're gone. From hard-scrabble Tennessee farms to upstate South Carolina mills, the women of this clan kept their heads up and their hands moving, quilting, cooking, and serving hot grits to hungry hoboes. Thanks to these clear-eyed, God-fearing women, their families survived fearsome poverty and a lacking education to endure the diseases and numbing physical labor of textile mills. Once so common, these Tales of a Cosmic Possum are fast becoming more uncommon. You'll want to celebrate them and their heroines again and again."

~ Aïda Rogers

Editor of the anthology series *State of the Heart: South Carolina Writers on the Places They Love*

TALES of a COSMIC POSSUM

From the Appalachia Mountains to the Cotton Mills

Sheila Ingle

Sheila Ingle

AMBASSADOR INTERNATIONAL
GREENVILLE, SOUTH CAROLINA & BELFAST, NORTHERN IRELAND
www.ambassador-international.com

Tales of a Cosmic Possum

From the Appalachia Mountains to the Cotton Mills

ISBN: 978-1-62020-612-6
eISBN:978-1-62020-690-4

"Eula," first published in the Savannah Anthology, Fall 2016, Honorable Mention Winner

Public Domain: "Let the Lower Lights Be Burning," "Beulah Land," "In the Sweet By and By," "When They Ring Those Golden Bells," "Will the Circle Be Unbroken?", "I Gotta Home in Glory Land," "Little Brown Jug," "Barbara Allen."

Cover Design and Page Layout by Hannah Nichols
eBook Conversion by Anna Riebe Raats
Author Photo by Betsy Neely Sikma

AMBASSADOR INTERNATIONAL
Emerald House
411 University Ridge, Suite B14
Greenville, SC 29601, USA
www.ambassador-international.com

AMBASSADOR BOOKS
The Mount
2 Woodstock Link
Belfast, BT6 8DD, Northern Ireland, UK
www.ambassadormedia.co.uk

The colophon is a trademark of Ambassador

For

Eula, Fannie, Lois, Lizzie, Mandy, Jenny Belle, Annie Mae, Julie

COSMIC POSSUM

A person whose roots are Appalachian, but who has gone on to become educated while still appreciating his or her mountain roots.

—Urban Dictionary

CONTENTS

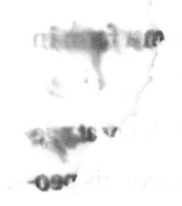

INTRODUCTION

The *Urban Dictionary* defines a cosmic possum as "a person whose roots are Appalachian, but who has gone on to become educated while still appreciating his or her mountain roots."

Tennessee poet Jane Hicks coined the term *cosmic possum* in her poem "How We Became Cosmic Possums." She adds that these men and women are the "first generation off the ridge or out of the holler." Hicks also says, "The possum is the perfect symbol of my beloved Appalachia: underappreciated, misunderstood, and the ultimate survivor in the face of all manners of predation" (see CosmicPossum.com).

Sharyn McCrumb used the expression, "cosmic possum," in her book, *The Songcatcher,* for the name of a hiker's hostel. When reading this novel about Appalachia, I stopped at this curious phrase to find out its meaning. And then, reality finally commanded my attention. I am married to a cosmic possum.

John William Ingle, my husband of now thirty-seven years, is the keeper of his family's stories. Living in Ingle Holler outside of Union, South Carolina, in the 1940s and 50s, was a microcosm of the Ingle Holler near Erwin, Tennessee. He grew up with grandparents, aunts, uncles, and a father who moved from the mountains. Lois Emory

Ingle, John's mother, was third generation Scots-Irish from a farm in North Carolina.

Leaving his family of cotton mill workers for the US Navy at age seventeen, he never returned to that life. But he never forgot his people or their culture. I enjoyed watching him reconnect with his upbringing. After attending a family reunion, his speech would become sprinkled with Appalachian sayings. He constantly gathered stories in his memory, which he shared with me and others. Never judging, he was, and still is, discovering and uncovering new tales to share.

This retired designer and pastel artist gathers his memories to crisscross a story, as a weaver unites various colors of threads on a loom. Sometimes the stories are humorous, and then there are the woeful ones. To help me record the lives of these strong Emory and Ingle women, he has reminisced with his brother, his cousins, and one surviving aunt.

John still enjoys country music, cornbread drenched with buttermilk, and the comfort of old blue jeans. He also likes attending the Little Theater and listening to Andrea Bocelli or Katherine Jenkins. He hated tending pigs when he was young, leaving that memory to the past. "Beulah Land" is still a much-loved hymn. Sometimes he will still sing his mother's favorite, "When They Ring Those Golden Bells." John's father, Oliver Edward Ingle, taught him auto mechanics, which have helped us with bills through the years. Our son is named Edward after his grandfather, and he changes the brakes on his truck, as he was taught. Specific mechanical and musical skills have now been passed down four generations.

I had the privilege of knowing Lois, Annie Mae, and Jenny Belle in their later years. The wrinkles in their brows, lack of makeup, disarrayed hair, fidgeting hands, and simple clothes advertised their mill village lives. But, oh, how I treasure the quilt that Lois/Mom hand sewed for us as a wedding gift. Listening to Jenny Belle pound out hymns on her piano entertained us one afternoon. When we went to see Annie Mae one Saturday, she served us that famous coconut cake with strong coffee. And each time we saw them, they shared new amusing anecdotes, along with Southern Appalachian hospitality.

As I have researched the cotton mills in Great Britain, the United States, and India, there are few differences. Churches, company stores, mill houses, and schools were available to the workers. Rivers and streams were the source of power for the mills. The work force included all family members that left the mountains and farm land for a weekly paycheck and cheap housing. Communities stood by and helped each other.

The cotton mills here in Upstate South Carolina, as well as in Northern states and other countries, are now deserted; vandals have burned some. Machines took over the jobs where people once stood; inventions and technology drastically changed the landscapes in the mills. Some mill village houses have been refurbished, but others have been razed to make room for more modern buildings. The abandoned buildings have become ghost towns.

Much has been lost from John's heritage and family. However, you, readers, can get a glimpse into the long days and short nights of a few forgotten women who labored in the cotton mills' spinning and weaving rooms and taught their daughters and nieces to follow their steps.

Without John's stories, the encouragement of my two friends Clare and Joyce, and helpful suggestions from our son Scott, their stories would have been lost. I admire their strength, creativity, and perseverance; now their lives in American history will not be forgotten.

FANNIE

When a touring circus came to town, schools and businesses closed. People lined the streets to watch the parade; wonder and curiosity filled the air. As the vibrantly costumed clowns marched, turned somersaults, and waved, children shrieked in delight. Powdered dogs and horses with their head plumes waving in the sky added to the grandeur. Acrobats tossed themselves in the air, and the man-who-swallowed-fire drew gasps of awe.

This free, titillating spectacle down every town's Main Street guaranteed paying customers for each performance during the circus' visit.

Charlie Sparks, the owner of Sparks World Famous Shows, made sure posters were plastered days in advance of his circus arriving in each town. On fences, available windows, or outside walls, pictures of elephants, lions, tigers, acrobats, and clowns publicized the event. The captions read, "A tremendous display of wealth and splendor" and, "Twenty-five years of honest dealing with the public," boldly describing his show to the community.

Charlie was the son of entertainers. Having lost both his parents at an early age, he was adopted by a family friend. This new household opened its first small circus in 1890 as a horse and wagon operation.

Charlie inherited the small show, and his business acumen expanded it into a fifteen-railcar circus.

Walking with the various acts in the parades and under the circus tents, Charlie always sported a Stetson hat and a cane. His other trademark was puffing a cigar.

This owner paid attention to his entertainers, the exotic animals, and their keepers. He demanded both man and beast be treated with respect and kindness.

On most of the posters was a picture of Mary, an Asian circus elephant; she was the star of the show. Bought when she was only four years old and four feet high, Mary had become a family pet, loved by Charlie and his wife, Addie.

Mary was larger than the Barnum and Bailey's star elephant called Jumbo, so her billing described her as "The Largest Living Land Animal on Earth." At eleven feet nine inches, she stood three inches taller than Jumbo and weighed over five tons. She had been trained to stand on her head and pitch a baseball. What's more, this talented elephant could play twenty-five tunes on the musical horns.

Because of her long twenty-two years of being schooled with positive reinforcement, she set an example for the other four elephants in this circus. Mary was the queen.

Mary always led the other pachyderms: Queen, Topsy, and babies, Ollie and Mutt, in the parades. Trunk to tail, they marched through each town. Charley's circus was popular in many small communities in Tennessee.

Erwin, Tennessee, in 1916, was a railroad town. It was the headquarters and repair facility for the Carolina, Clinchfield, and Ohio railroads. The brick depot stood in a noteworthy spot on Main

Street; the passenger station took up two stories, and the depot only one. Traveling from Spartanburg, South Carolina, to Elkhorn City, Kentucky, this short line rail streamed through the mountains. Even with the fifty-five tunnels on its route, the coal-stoked engine moved forward daily.

Located in the Cherokee National Forest, the town rested in a valley surrounded by mountains: Buffalo Mountain in the north, Rich Mountain in the west, and Unaka Mountain in the south. Meeting in this valley were the Nolichucky River and the North Indian Creek. Because of the former Cherokee Indian settlements in this area, the original settlers used native names when first identifying the region. Nolichucky River Gorge with its rapids was a favorite scenic route for the passengers on the trains.

The town was laid out five blocks long and three blocks wide. A blacksmith owned the livery stable, and he stayed busy. Across the street was the Bank of Erwin, established in 1909; it was an imposing building with columns. Churches, a large mansion or two, and two-story businesses were randomly scattered throughout. First Baptist Church was on the corner of Main and Love Street; a large bell rang on Sundays to remind parishioners of the hour. The Love family donated the land on the corner of Main and Depot to First Christian Church.

The town granted franchises for lights, water, and telephones by 1915, but not all received these services in the outlying area. John Wheeler Price owned the general store on Main, and he rented space to Richard Britton, the barber, for his one chair. J. C. White operated a jewelry and watch repair shop. With World War I raging in Europe, "making do" was the standard of living. Bartering chickens or quarts of homemade molasses paid for services rendered. Dr. Joseph Lane worked out of his home, as did the lawyer, Mr. Samuel Lee. [illegible]

A new Unicoi County courthouse was built in 1915. Surrounded by a low concrete wall, this two-story brick structure, topped with a cupola, graced another corner on Main Street. The metal flagpole identified this building as a seat of government, and the raising and lowering of the United States flag was more than a daily ritual. The town was proud of their twentieth century structure and proud to be Americans.

Built in 1899, the Unaka Springs Hotel was a three-story wood frame resort. Many doctors, lawyers, bankers, and railroad management chose it because of its gracious staff, mineral-rich water, and stylish accommodations. Besides its popular health offerings, the hotel offered entertainment: croquet, miniature golf, and dancing. Reasonable, but not low-priced rooms, were two dollars per night and ten dollars for a week's sojourn.

Guests depended on the railroad to reach the hotel. In fact, neighboring family groups rode in for picnic lunches and later traveled home the same way. Without the passenger cars, visitors had to ford the river or struggle down a steep cliff path.

This insignificant Tennessee town provided little to either build or promote a large population. Small farms, small businesses, and small stills scattered the lumpy bottoms.

An estimated 2,500 residents lived in and around Erwin, and all appeared to be congregated en masse on this September 13, 1916, at the railroad yard.

A mixed bag of professionals and farmers stood shoulder to shoulder, each one peering around the heads of those in front.

Pomade kept the men's hair in place. Creased fedoras stood out from the farmers' well-worn straw hats. Dirty and clean bandanas were pulled out of back pockets.

Farm women, wearing sunbonnets, shawls, and aprons, huddled with other womenfolk attired in dresses with shorter hemlines, wide collars, and oversize hats. World War I had already had an impact on clothing; rationed fabric was more expensive. Bobbed hair styles were popular, but the country women still wore their long hair pulled up in buns or twists on their heads.

Muted conversations were carried on around when children were near. Adults were unsure of the anticipated event; many wondered why they were even there.

Fannie Ingle carried her son, Floyd, around the edges of the crowd in the railroad yard. He held tightly to her neck and hid his face. The loud talk and pushing of the countless people scared the four-year-old, and he held his thumb tightly in his mouth.

"Howdy, Fannie." Fannie's former schoolteacher, Louise Allen, patted her on the shoulder. "I swanee I'm so glad to see you. How are you? And how's that sweet boy of yours doin'?"

With a welcoming smile on her face, Fannie turned to her.

"I be plumb fine. Reckin this here young'un keeps me busy. He's sharp as a tack and into everything."

Louise Allen was the teacher for the upper grades in Erwin. She had been trained at the Asheville Normal and Collegiate Institute. This school prepared young women from the southern Appalachians to teach in the rural schools.

In 1870, Lewis Pease and his wife moved to Asheville, North Carolina, from New York City. While in New York, this couple established a school in the challenging Five Points community. Pease believed that education and training for jobs was the answer to keeping children and adults from turning to crime. In Asheville, he soon founded the Pease Industrial School and then donated land for the Normal and Collegiate Institute in 1892.

Dr. Thomas Lawrence directed the Normal with the support of the Presbyterian Board of Home Missions. The word normal came from the French words *école normale,* meaning a model school. That first year, the student body enrolled 110 students; they ranged in age from five to twenty.

The four-story wood frame building bustled with activity as the girls moved from class to class. Required subjects were typical liberal arts courses, but courses in carpentry, weaving, cooking, music, and sewing were also mandatory. This practical knowledge and training graduated students who were encouraged to make the communities where they taught a better place.

Louise had grown up outside of Asheville and had always wanted to be a teacher. As a child, when she wasn't busy with household chores, she set up a school next to the fireplace. Her students were cornhusk dolls that she made herself. She counted her profession as a privilege and opportunity to stretch the minds of the children in urban communities.

Reading was her hobby and obsession. For all occasions, she asked for books. It had broken her heart to lose Fannie in sixth grade as one of her students.

With Louise were her six-year-old twins, Sally and Lucy. Curly blonde hair escaped the ribbons in their braids. Their Mary Janes were scuffed, but both blue gingham dresses with the wide sailor collars, trimmed in white, were clean and neat, though worn. Louise's husband, Richard, worked for the railroad as a coal stoker and collected $760 a year for his labor. Her teaching salary of $257 annually helped with the household expenses.

The two girls started playing peekaboo with Floyd as their mothers talked. Before long, all three frolicked with the game of leapfrog. Floyd was tall for his age, so he had no trouble putting his chubby hands on their backs and leaping over their heads. Ignoring the milling crowd of adults, they entertained themselves, as they had been taught to do.

"'Aire ye still areadin' ever' day?" asked Fannie.

She loved a good yarn and was intrigued with characters and how they acted.

"Oh, yes," Louise replied. "That is still my favorite part of the school day! I mind you'd like the book we're in the middle of readin' now."

"*The Wonderful Wizard of Oz* was the best'est! Thet Dor'thy follered her own lights and did a heap of good in that world of talkin' animals, scarecrows, and a tin man. She warn't no feardy cat and kep' on foller'n' 'at yallar road. Served that mean ol' witch right to melt clean away when Dorothy doused her with water. I shore wuz tickled thet she and 'at dog Toto headed back home."

Louise was stunned with the young woman's memories of a novel she heard only one time five years ago. Smiling at her former pupil, the teacher continued, "Two weeks ago, I started readin' *Anne of Green Gables*. Anne is an orphan that has lived in many places. Marilla and Matthew Cuthbert are sister and brother who live on a family farm. Matthew needs help because he is getting older. They decide to adopt a boy to help them, but the orphanage sends Anne Shirley instead.

"Redheaded Anne jaws all the time. She calls Matthew a kindred spirit, and the prim Marilla decides her influence on Anne will help her. Anne breaks her slate over Gilbert Blythe's head because he teasingly calls her 'carrots,' and she can't forgive him. She thinks he's too big for his britches and stays riled at him."

Fannie listened to every word of the synopsis, thinking that this Anne had gumption to spare.

"Oh, Fannie, she hates her red hair so badly that she tries to dye it black, and it ends up green! Can you imagine what green hair must look like?"

They both laughed.

A loud voice in front of them interrupted their catching up. In front of the two mothers, the town's barber poked his neighbor in the ribs, exclaiming, "Thar be the elephants. Big Mary is leadin' the little 'uns, jest like always."

Only four days before, Mary had killed her new handler, Red Eldridge, in Kingsport, Tennessee, forty miles away from Erwin.

The elephants had performed well in the big top in Kingsport. With little prodding, they walked around the ring as the band played. Sitting in the red-and-gold saddles on each elephant was a trainer, and a headdress of artificial blue feathers was tied on the huge mammal heads.

They continued their routine with sitting on their haunches and standing on their heads. The audience cheered, as they formed a train. In the lead was Mary; the other four, in order from largest to smallest, positioned their front legs on each other's backs. Leisurely walking around the ring, they raised their trunks and trumpeted for the applauding crowd.

Red rode Mary out of the big top to a watering hole in between shows. The other elephants had their own trainers and followed.

Walking her leisurely pace on the way back to the circus tent, Mary spied a piece of watermelon on the side of the road. She followed her nose, changed directions, and plodded toward the fruit.

Ignoring Red's shouts to halt, he prodded her with the elephant stick. Still intent on her course for a snack, the inexperienced man then goaded the elephant in her ear with the bull hook.

The three-foot-long pole, with its sharp metal hook on the end, triggered severe pain.

The furious and wounded Mary grabbed Red around the waist with her trunk and threw him against a drink stand.

This angered toss knocked the side out of the stand.

Mary walked steadily over to the man and set her foot on his head until it was flat.

Shock and panic ensued. Watching the lumbering elephants drinking and spraying the water in the air drew families to the spot, but it was the murder that filled Kingsport with shudders, gasps, and screams. Mothers covered their children's eyes and hustled them away. The men stepped forward and formed a barrier against another possible attack.

The nonstop bedlam continued; the adults were in protective stance. Some took up the cry of "Kill the elephant." The blacksmith, Hench Cox, shot five rounds at Mary, but his bullets didn't faze her.

Minutes felt longer to the bystanders, until Charlie Sparks arrived. He calmed the restless animal that was swaying back and forth in repetitive motions.

Mayor Miller ordered Sheriff Hickman to arrest Mary. Charlie led her to the county jail and staked her outside. Heavy metal chains circled one front leg and the alternate back leg for control. Viewers stayed a safe distance from the killer elephant.

A closed-door meeting between Charlie, the sheriff, and the mayor lasted only a brief time. Charlie knew that Mary was now a liability to the circus; it was inevitable that the elephant would have to be destroyed. Neither the crowd of spectators outside or future audiences in other towns would allow for any other verdict.

Sheriff Hickman explained that a gun big enough to put the animal down was not available. Mayor Miller remembered that Erwin had a crane in their railroad yard that could lift locomotive boilers. Phone calls and arrangements were completed with the town of Erwin.

The next day, Charlie's circus performed in Erwin. Mary, without her saddle or blue plumes, was staked outside the tent. After the show, Mary led the other elephants one more time down Love Street to the railroad.

Excitement built in the crowd as the elephants arrived. All could see the lofty crane suspended in the air, but not everyone had a glimpse of the animals. It was a gathering of 2,500 strong for this hanging of a murderer on September 16, 1916.

In the midst of this throng stood Fannie and Louise.

The two women heard the elephants' cries as the four younger ones were led away. Mary trumpeted a few times. These animals sensed a change. Mary, Queen, Topsy, Ollie, and Mutt had formed a family that stuck together.

Big Mary
(source: public domain)

Sounds of scuffling feet and murmured voices were background for the naïve children's play.

"Look 'e thar!" a startled man loudly declared. "That thangamabob is pullin' her up!"

Even to the limits of the crowd, all could see Big Mary being tugged into the air by the chain around her neck.

Gasps, cries, and unknown sounds mushroomed through the crowd. Hands reached to cover already shut eyes. The tremor was collective.

Someone forgot to undo the chain around her leg; it was attached to a rail to keep her in place while the other elephants were led away. The crane lifted her up, but then loud noises of her bones and ligaments snapping and cracking could be heard.

Those in the front of the crowd were horrified, and revolted screams burst into the air. The chain broke, but it was quickly reattached to the groaning animal.

"What's happenin'?" Fannie tapped the tall stranger in front of her. "Can't see nary a thang."

He turned and quietly remarked, "Thay's gonna do hit agin."

And they did. Once more, the crane lifted Mary up, and within minutes, she died. Erwin had hung an elephant. A veterinarian pronounced her dead.

The same tall stranger swiveled his head again. "She didn't even put up no ruckus."

Fannie turned to Louise with questions in her eyes. Then she looked down at Floyd and the girls, who were oblivious to what had taken place.

"Shore am glad my boy warn't payin' no attention. Wouldn't want him to carry that thar picture 'round with him."

Louise answered, "Not so sure I cotton to this hangin' of an elephant, even if it did murder that man. Seems like there should be a place reserved for ornery and old animals to live out their days."

As the crowd moved away from the scene of the elephant hanging in the sky, there was much shaking of heads and mumbles about this deed. It just didn't seem suiting. Few stayed to watch the grave dug in front of the railroad shop doors for Mary; they had seen enough. Stoic men and edgy women turned away from the scene that was no longer a circus.

Louise reached out her arms to Fannie, and the younger mother walked into them. These mountain folk were, as a general rule, not emotional; they tended to bury their feelings and ponder them later. Fannie's tears touched a chord in Louise's heart.

"I'm wrung out and upsot," Fannie flatly stated and fell silent in Louise's kind embrace.

Then backing up and straightening her shoulders, Fannie continued, "That shor'nuf skeered the livin'daylights outta me. Is thar book larnin' to hep a body unnerstan' sech a show?"

Louise furrowed her brow and shook her head. "Men make bad decisions all the time, and I believe we only this minute saw another one. Fear can take a spell to get over for a person to think straight again. Not even books can lend us a hand on that'n."

Gathering her twins in front of her, she encouraged them to be polite and say good-by. The girls deferred to their mother, and each grabbed for one of her hands.

Before the three were lost in the crowd, Louise turned back once again.

"Great day in the morning! I don't know why I didn't think of this sooner. When you're in town next time, drop by my house for a spell. You can borrow one of my books and take it home."

Encouraging Fannie with a smile, Louise added, "I'll be watching for you."

* * *

A few onlookers, still mesmerized by the hanging of an animal, lagged behind. Justice had been served, but its rightness was unconventional. Talking and pointing to the dead elephant with the chain around its neck, some continued to gawk. Fannie had seen enough.

With tears still trickling down her face, the sixteen-year-old mother hesitantly hiked toward home. She held her four-year-old's chubby hand tight in her own. Fannie and her son walked away from the hanging of Mary, the circus elephant.

Muted by the spectacle, Fannie turned around once and noticed the deep shadows behind the elephant's body and over the train derrick that served as her gallows. Public hangings were not unusual in Tennessee for men who had broken the law and deserved the death penalty. This execution appeared different and shameful to Fannie.

As with many fall days in the Appalachian region, skies were still overcast. The all-night rain the night before was a common occurrence. Swirls of yellow, ochre, and brown leaves stirred and fell on the muddy clay street and wooden sidewalks.

No money jingled in Fannie's pocket for the town trolley, but mother and son were comfortable with walking everywhere they went. Both were barefoot, and their clothes were patched, but clean.

Mountain people in Appalachia had few possessions, but were content with what they had. They lived the way past generations had lived and survived.

Fannie's faded gingham dress hung loosely on her slight frame. Once upon a time, it was blue and had a string belt; that was when it was her mother's dress. The hem showed signs of restitching, and the white collar was dingy. A thin handkerchief peeked out of the right side pocket.

Down her back hung Fannie's braided black hair; a short shoelace held it together. Her hair pulled straight back revealed her oval face and made her eyes more prominent. Those deep-set blue eyes disclosed a profound sorrow beyond her sixteen years.

One of Floyd's galluses on his overalls slipped off his shoulder and fell down to his elbow; the child didn't notice. Little bothered him; he tended to be easygoing and amicable. He liked the patches Fannie sewed on his clothes when needed. Since he had played outdoors all summer, there were many squares, as well as stains, to decorate them now.

Following directions was difficult for Floyd. He was slow to crawl and walk. Over and over, Fannie and her family would name household and farm objects for the boy, but for him to imitate them was difficult. Floyd understood words and phrases long before he voiced them himself. The whole family protected the youngster; outsiders weren't as kind.

A woman at church once shook her head at Fannie and said, "Yer a mollycoddling thet chile. Ye' orter let him do it hisself!"

Another day, she saw some children pointing at Floyd. He was sitting on the steps of the general store slowly eating an apple. He took time to examine the apple in between bites and then would deliberately choose a place to taste its sweetness once again.

"Fer shore, he's dumber'n a coal bucket," one unaware boy said, and they all laughed.

For now, Floyd put his thumb in his mouth and walked slower. All he saw around him momentarily captured his attention. His diminutive body regularly turned back and forth to observe whatever his eyes saw.

Because she was mulling over what they had scarcely walked away from, Fannie chose not to hurry him up.

The two turned at the sound of a car's horn behind them. A maximum speed of 10 miles per hour was the law in Erwin's business district, but pedestrians and horse-drawn wagons were still warned by most drivers.

Fannie wondered what *The Erwin Weekly Magnet* would print in tomorrow's paper about today's events. J. F. Toney was the editor, and his news was never trifling. Known as a straight shooter, he stayed away from gossip. The young girl hoped there wouldn't be a picture of the poor animal.

She knew her older brother Make was in the throng of watchers somewhere, but she never saw him. He had a load of logs to deliver to the train today, and he kept his commitments. His logging business fed his family.

Fannie wanted to talk to him; he never made fun of her questions. Though Make was married with children of his own, he looked out for her and Floyd.

Letting go of Floyd's hand, she said, "Floyd, let's us race! Last'n to the end o' this hyer sidewalk's a rotten aig."

"Gotta eetch, Momma!" the boy jumped, jerked, and tried to scratch his back. "Hep me! Some big critter bit me!"

"My goodness gracious, son! Jist a cotton pickin' minute! Ye gotta stay still."

Floyd circled around his mother, as he tried to reach his itching place. Fannie finally grabbed his wiry body and proceeded to scratch the pitiful child's back with her broken fingernails. He was like a worm in hot ashes, as he wiggled and squealed.

Finally his show was over, and the two children, Fannie and Floyd, took off down the sidewalk, shrieking as they ran. When the walkway ended, they jumped onto the clay and hurried on.

The dirt road was narrow in places, and potholes of all sizes and shapes were numerous. Soggy leaves led to spills by Floyd, but they laughingly pressed on. Fannie would snatch him up and place him solidly on his feet before they started again. Even though he was used to falling, his mother fussed over him.

Their dash eventually ended at a cabin on Green Knob Mountain.

Fannie's parents, William Gaither Ingle and his wife, Jane Elizabeth, farmed on the lower side of the smaller Green Knob next to Polly Erwin Mountain near the North Indian Creek. They raised tobacco as their money crop, and their land abundantly yielded corn, barley, beans, okra, and tomatoes for sale or barter. The bottom land was rich in nutrients. Jane Elizabeth grew watermelon in her garden patch to make watermelon preserves to sell at the farmer's market. Their barnyard and pastures were filled with chickens, cows, goats, horses, and mules.

Resisting change and satisfied with the status quo, as were most Appalachians, Gaither and Lizzie lived as his grandparents had in Buncombe County, North Carolina. Believing in God's providence, they were independent and distrusted strangers. Helping others in need was a way of life, and the couple never missed an opportunity. Whether it was honey from his bee hives, a basket of his tomatoes, or a jug of his moonshine, Gaither was openhanded.

This Ingle couple lived off the land and raised eight children by working their parcel on a daily basis. Each member, no matter the age, had regular assigned tasks to accomplish. The family depended on each other for their well-being, and laziness was not tolerated.

Gaither earned cash money from his honey and homebrew.

He built ten wooden box hives for his bees. William placed each hive on a frame to keep them off the ground. Bees were defenseless against damp ground or critters. They were positioned near a copse of trees in the sun. Needing protection from the rain and wind, the trees gave them that shield. Since bees require daily water, he had replaced the hives close to one of the many springs on his property. Setting their hives away from animals and people also kept the bees happy. They required privacy to flourish.

Because William knew bears would seek out hives in their home range, he was careful to watch for any threatening activity. He quickly harvested the honey after the spring, summer, and fall nectar fell. The hunting bears particularly were a nuisance before and after their hibernation.

Bears prefer the new bees and eggs to the honey. The honey was a sweet reward. Full of protein and fat, the young insects were a tasty treat worth the stings from the older ones. Protecting their hives from a marauding bear, adult bees will sting a bear's face and ears. A bear's fur will protect the rest of its body.

One day, William laughed at a black bear shaking bees out of her fur like she would shake water. Clacking their teeth in fear, her two cubs rolled in the grass, as bees circled them. Despite the size difference, the smallest buzzing bees drove away all three animals.

Another time, a curious bear meandered into the small building where William's copper still was set up. The bear's unique sensitivity to smell led him to investigate. Before long, he had knocked over the still, raided the ground for food, and then proceeded to knock over various pots and barrels. Not finding a food interest, he ambled out in search of more lucrative victuals.

William's still was housed first in a lean-to not far from their house, but demand for his white lightning caused him to build a one-room cabin for his trade. Close to another spring, the field of corn, and his house fashioned a convenient home business.

Raising additional corn each year was essential to this operation. Regular customers depended on him. Because of the careful distilling process he had perfected, his corn mash would make new recipes of moonshine up to eight times. His own Appalachian spring water and heirloom corn were his secret ingredients. William's clientele grew through the years, as other connoisseurs heard of his smooth, sweet, and spicy beverage.

By taking only a few stops to sit down and catch their breaths, Fannie and Floyd arrived in record time to the two-story farm house of five rooms.

Her father used the skills he learned from his father to construct his home. He felled the trees off his land, hauled them to the site, and cut them to size, all backbreaking work. In a wagon, he brought rocks from the river and fields to make the stilts and fireplaces. Mud was the mortar. Small windows and a short door helped with insulation.

Gaither whittled pegs for the inside of the house and for the porch. The pegs held clothing, strings of drying beans, cooking pots, and tools. Besides their individual chores, the Ingle children worked together to gather chestnuts, dig ginseng roots, and gather ramps to sell.

The family labored together to keep the wolf from the door.

A porch ran across the front of the house, and hanging on the clothes line was the typical Wednesday laundry. It was still damp, but not soggy, because of the weather. Fannie knew it would be her job to take it down and fold it later.

Come rain or shine, dirty clothes became clean laundry on Wednesday and Saturday, and were hung on the front porch from a rope. Pillow slips, overalls, socks, and underwear all greeted visitors on those days.

Fannie immediately smiled at the two Mason jars full of her mother's sunflowers. They were sitting on the top step to the porch. Bees, butterflies, and birds all hovered close to the fall blooms. These happy flowers spread every year and had to be separated. Bright yellow rays surrounded the dark brown centers and welcomed all.

Floyd stretched his legs and arms to go up the steps on all fours. Even though he was panting from the race home, he refused to quit until he fell onto the porch floor. Sitting down with a loud plump on his bottom, his small presence drove the insects and birds away.

Fannie noted his perseverance with a pat on his head and encouragement. "You hightailed it home today! I'm right proud."

Hearing her mother's clear voice singing her favorite hymn, Fannie sat beside her son and softly accompanied her mother.

Brightly beams our Father's mercy,
From His lighthouse evermore,
But to us He gives the keeping
Of the lights along the shore.

Let the lower lights be burning!
Send a gleam across the wave!
Some poor struggling, fainting seaman
You may rescue, you may save.

Dark the night of sin has settled,
Loud the angry billows roar;
Eager eyes are watching, longing,
For the lights along the shore.

Trim your feeble lamp, my brother;
Some poor sailor, tempest-tossed,
Trying now to make the harbor,
In the darkness may be lost.

Let the lower lights be burning!
Send a gleam across the wave!
Some poor struggling, fainting seaman
You may rescue, you may save.

Lizzie Ingle smiled. "Hello, my darlin' daughter and grandson, come tell me about yourn mornin'." Glancing at her daughter's solemn face as the two walked in the front door, Lizzie sought a clue in her own mind as to what was disturbing her youngest today. How the mother wished that Fannie's life had gone differently.

Sometimes her hurt turned to ire, and she had murderous thoughts against the man who took her child's innocence. Lizzie helped twelve-year-old Fannie in her delivery of Floyd, and it was a struggle she still had nightmares about. Fannie was small and undeveloped, and Floyd had broad shoulders. The blood loss was great, and the healing was long. Damage assured that Fannie would have no more children.

"Oh, Laws a' mercy! It must have been a terrible sight," exclaimed Lizzie.

Lizzie had seen and experienced tragedy in her life. She would never search disaster out and had learned acceptance of what she could not change. Watching a hanging was not her idea of entertainment.

As Floyd wandered over to inspect and taste the warm cookies on the counter, Fannie rolled her eyes in his direction.

Responding to her mother, but speaking softly, Fannie said, "I like ta' died. The hangin' tuck two times. Don't know why I went thar.

But, Mammy, I got to visit with my teacher, Miz Louise. Her girls and Floyd played, even w' no play purties about. She's gonna give me a book to read. One o' her very own books, jist like I was her kin!"

"God works in mysterious ways, Fannie. Shore know that to be the gospel truth," replied Lizzie. "Foller yer own lights, child."

* * *

Several years later, Fannie Mae Ingle and her son, Floyd, moved to Union, South Carolina, to work in the Union Mill. Her brother Make built them a house beside him in Ingle Holler. When he was ten, Floyd started work in the mill with his mother. Fannie filled batteries; she placed empty bobbins on the spinning frame to be filled anew with thread. Floyd started work as a sweeper and retired as one.

Fannie was independent; she planted a vegetable garden every spring and canned the extra. Since there was a wild cherry tree nearby, she crafted wine from the fruit for her personal use. Floyd picked wild berries and fruit for her to cook preserves and jelly.

Between her hard work at the mill and living off the land, as her parents taught her, mother and son had few needs. Fannie never married.

AMANDA

Balancing with her right elbow, Mandy Moseley carefully stepped down each of the narrow stairs. The steep and dark stairwell was treacherous for the gray-haired woman with the curved shape. Her son-in-law kept them in fine repair, but her bowed body was tested daily in this step-by-step journey.

The mill houses were standard. Constructed for two families, they were compact two-story duplexes. A thin wall down the center of the steps separated the households, and a wide porch extended across the front. Chairs and buckets of flowers welcomed visitors.

Mandy marked her footstep rhythm with the black cane gripped tightly in her left hand. Thump! Thump! Thump!

Her soft but fervent morning song touched her daughter's listening heart.

O Beulah Land, sweet Beulah Land,
As on thy highest mount I stand,
I look away across the sea,
Where mansions are prepared for me,
And view the shining glory shore,
My Heav'n, my home forever more!

Mandy's repertoire of songs was limited to those she grew up listening to in Queen Hollow. The eerie blue mists of the Great Smoky Mountains hovered over the family's one-room cabin and farm. Isolated by the peaks and valleys in the North Carolina range, the clan inhabited the land and culture of their Scot-Irish ancestors.

Her only daughter, Amanda, named for her mother, pushed her stitching out of her lap and jumped from the rocking chair to help the crippled fifty-two-year-old safely manage the last step. Mandy's work days on the farm and the mill were over. She now earned her keep by watching her three grandchildren while their parents worked in Clifton #2.

"That's my bonny girl," said Mandy. The painful swelling of rheumatism plagued her joints whether she moved or held still. Her hands and feet were red and stiff. When the rain fell, her symptoms worsened.

Rather than the daughter holding onto her mother, Mandy tightly grabbed her daughter's arm for extra support for the walk to the kitchen table.

"I's afeared I couldn't git outta bed today. Pushin' them kivers back wus a mite tryin', as usual. Fetchin' my clothes wuz near a stumblin' block, fer shore," the feisty little woman continued. "Gumption, my friend, gumption, led me right down them steps this here mornin'."

Nodding her head in pride over her mother's battle victories, Amanda poured two cups of coffee into their cherished, chipped blue cups. The matching saucers were long gone. Her china was a hodgepodge of patterns and pieces bought at the company store. All had missing parts, but buying new was not an option. Only necessities were included in the weekly budget, and replacing damaged dishes was never on the list.

Mother and daughter sat in silence, savoring it before the day began its bustle. Flickering light from the kerosene lamp on the table was the only break in the darkness. Amanda noticed the globe needed cleaning; distinctive finger smudges smeared the glass. Picking up a damp dish cloth on the table, she wiped the marks away.

The porcelain pot on the wood stove perked a mouthwatering brew. Neither woman doctored their many cups of coffee, but drank it black. It was 4:30 on Saturday morning. Soon Amanda would leave to catch the trolley to work.

The Pacolet River was around fifty miles long. A Vermont native, Dexter Edgar Converse, led the Clifton Manufacturing company and built its first mill at Hurricane Shoals. Operation began in 1881 on Clifton #1, and life on the meandering and quiet river changed. Dams harnessed the water, and advertisements brought in families of workers from North Carolina, Virginia, and Tennessee. Leaving hardscrabble lives on small farms, an assured weekly paycheck was security to bring them to the Upstate of South Carolina.

Clifton #2 began operation in 1889, and once again operatives flocked to the river mills for promises of work and cheap housing. Schools, churches, and stores built by the mill tied the people to the industry. Then in 1895, the third mill opened. On trains and in wagons, families again arrived to work full-time in another new cotton mill.

The two women reveled in the few moments of companionable silence. Usually this time of year, they took their first cup of coffee to the front porch to watch dawn break over the river.

There was no sunrise to enjoy this June 6, 1903, morning. It was a dreary morning. For three days, rain had fallen steadily on their four-room house on the hill above the Pacolet River. Now the downpour was hard and fierce; it pounded and pummeled the house.

When Amanda left for her mill shift, then her husband, John, would come in to sleep. Since Mandy lived with them, there was always an adult to tend the children. Not all the mill families had a built-in sitter, and Mandy minded any extras that showed up.

When the children weren't running and playing outside, Mandy entertained them with her storytelling. She always started her tales with "When Heck was a pup," and the children knew the happenings were a long time ago. Most of her stories dealt with the Appalachian people and their ways. Haints, granny women, and talking animals were main characters. Settings were in a holler or yonder over a mountain. The enthralled children hung on Mandy's every look and phrase.

Amanda stood up to leave and walked over to the window to look out. All of her flowers had fallen off the porch rail, and she could see the angry, river water creeping up the bank toward her front steps. Her plans for a Sunday family picnic on the rocks were not going to be possible. Her three children, Boyd, Charlie, and Julie, would be cooped up once again in the house.

"This chunk washer is agonna destroy my garden. Plantin' on Good Friday ain't agonna protect my vegetables from all this rain," remarked the young woman. "It's a'rainin' them cats-and-dogs we heard tell about!"

Smoothing a worn patch down on her faded blue-and-white gingham dress, Amanda thought about how she could remake her outfit into a shirt for John. All her patching would not bother him.

Hopping and squealing as only a six-year-old girl could, Julie bounded down those same stairs. Her light-brown hair was tousled and fell into her face.

"Mama! Granny! My birthday! I'm right ready."

In her short gown, she dashed from one to another to share her hugs and excitement. Julie grabbed her mother's hands, and they danced around both the kitchen and living room.

Stopping to catch her breath, Amanda picked up the wiggling child. "Julie, my sweet girl! Happy birthday! Yer like our new friend Dorothy in *The Wizard of Oz.* You's borned excited about ever'thing. We'll read another chapter tonight afore we eat your birthday cake."

Mandy added, "Lawsy, child, climb up hyer on m' lap. Let's set a spell and talk over what we will be busy about today. I reckin we must bake y'ur favorite pound cake."

Abruptly the front door banged open, and the wind followed John Petty into his house. His slicker was drenched, and water streamed off his wide brim hat. Blowing rain chased him, as well as wet leaves and small branches. He wasted no words.

"Git up the stairs! To the roof! The river's afloodin'!"

They could all hear the crash of water outside and saw streams of the Pacolet River running across the porch. Beyond the open door was a flood of water shifting and journeying toward their home.

Julie slid off her grandmother's lap and screamed. She kept on screaming.

John ran to Mandy, scooped her up in both arms, and headed for the stairs. Taking them two at a time, he didn't pause to pick up her cane.

He hollered up the stairs to his sons, Boyd and Charlie, "Climb out your window, boys. Git in that tree!"

Amanda followed him with the wide-eyed and trembling Julie in her arms.

"Pa, what's that noise?" shouted Boyd, at his door, and then obeyed his father.

Close to the children's bedroom window that they shared with their grandmother was a tall oak tree. Its branches were strong, as well as its roots. Boyd and Charlie had climbed onto it many times in secret but had never been told to climb onto its branches.

Peering out the window, the ten-and eight-year-old boys saw flood waters covering about ten feet of the trunk. They hesitated and then heard their father yell once more.

"Git, boys, you can do it! I know you can. I'm right behind you!"

John was the night watchman for Clifton #2, and he carried a Smith and Wesson. His family respected and trusted him, as did the mill village. Knowing it was time for his wife and two boys to leave for work, he had raced the morass of flood waters and the deluge to reach his home.

Sloshing through mud and pools of water, he shouted at families about the rising waters along the way. He beat the forty-foot wall of water that merely scraped his house. The flood buried other homes.

The house swayed, and fear prodded the boys to jump onto the branch closest to them. John stepped long onto that same branch and put Mandy down in the crux of the tree. He turned quickly to reach for Amanda's hand. She had thrown Julie up on her shoulder and was ready for his helping hand.

Seconds, which seemed like hours, now found the Moseley family safe in an oak tree. John covered Mandy and Amanda with his slicker. Julie curled up in her mother's lap. Amanda put her arm around her mother. Three generations huddled together.

Two raccoons clinched another branch. The boys stared at the animals they shared a roost with. Four masked eyes stared back. No one was leaving the shared sanctuary.

In the afternoon of June 5, the creeks of Spivey's, Motlow, and Obed creeks raised the level of the Pacolet River ten feet over its normal level. Then around 3:00 in the morning of June 6, a small tornado accompanied by a powerful cloudburst, hit in the Campobello area. The deadly strength of all this water swiftly attacked and swept the valley.

The family saw bales of cotton and pieces of spindles floating in the water from Clifton No. 3. It had trembled, and then the five-story 50,000-spindle mill dropped. When its dam gave way, the water rose about forty feet in only a few minutes.

With a wide grin, Charlie poked his older brother. "Now how're we gonna go to work today!"

Boyd quizzically looked at the river. "Reckin not. That water's shore angry."

Both worked as sweepers in the cotton mill where their parents worked. Their school days were over, because the family needed many paychecks to survive from week to week.

They could hear the screams of their neighbors and dogs howling. Wind swayed the tree branches of their perch. That pleasant river that welcomed visitors to swim, fish, and climb its huge rocks had changed into a monstrous beast. The river swept a parade of destruction and catastrophe in front of them.

Homes below their house closest to its banks disappeared. Mill house roofs, planks of the mill floors, and the timbers of William Harden's grist mill floated past them.

Chickens in their coops and two cows, perched unsteadily on a roof, sank not far from shore.

Clifton Mill #1 soared past. Part of the building collapsed, and three men fell in the swirling river with the debris. There had been warnings to this mill of the flood, but no time to race the thundering water.

Terrified families, sitting on their roofs, were tossed and turned by the strength and force of a river out of control. Cries for help resounded over the river's own roar. John Merchant yelled to the heavens when he saw his sister, her husband, and three children swept away. He was helpless.

"Amanda," John whispered to his wife. "I run past the comp'ny store. The water wuz up to the second floor where Hicks Stribling lives. He was up in a tree. Poor man was nekkid as a jay bird. Hopin' someone heped git him down."

Minutes passed, and the river continued to spread. On a normal day, it was 100 feet wide where they lived. The Pacolet River reached the banks, covered the huge rocks, and continued to rise until it covered more than 500 feet. Snakes and a rooster now joined the Petty's in their safe haven.

"Look, Papa," Boyd pointed up the river.

A black man was rescuing people off the roofs. He steered a cotton bale raft out into the water, picked a stranded person off a roof, and navigated back to shore. Over and over, he navigated this same mercy mission. Steadily and with confidence, the rescuer saved life

The Pacolet Flood

after life. Boyd and Charlie watched intently and started shouting "hooray" each time another one made his way safely to shore.

Horror choked the minds and hearts of the three adults. Awe and wonder cloaked the children.

Then half of the four stories of their mill, Clifton #2, also rocketed by.

Seventeen-year-old George Willis and one of his friends rescued a woman hanging on to cordwood in the water. They threw her a well rope, pulled her close to shore, and then carried her packsaddle to higher ground.

John could stand it no longer. His family was safe, but there were many who weren't. Turning to Amanda, he said, "I need to help. Awful bad out there, shuga'."

"Boyd, pay attention now. You in charge. Don't be afeared, and jist mind your ma. I'll be back directly." John handed his soaking hat to his son and patted both boys on their shoulders.

He reached out and kissed Amanda's cheek. "I swan I'll be back afore long."

Amanda grabbed his hand with both of hers and tightly squeezed it. She mouthed the words "I love you more."

John jumped and hit the water hard. He went under but fought the angry river until his head was above the waves. Then he started swimming up the bank to higher and drier ground. Standing in mud, he waved back to his kin. He saw that Boyd had put on his hat; his oldest had understood his father's message.

"Momma." Amanda turned to her mother. "You finished three more quilts last week, and the cedar chest is slap full of others. I figure we can make pallets all over our bedrooms for those who have lost their home. We still have the fixin's for some big pots of soup. We have eggs and milk to make cornbread. So many are gonna be in a fix, and there is a heap we can do."

"The Good Book tells us to trust. Some of those poor folk are gonna need a heap of trusting, and we git to hep them along," Mandy smiled at the thoughts of opening up their home. "I always did hanker to openin' up a boardin' house."

As the women started planning, the night watchman joined others who were making rafts from the cotton bales. The men tied ropes to the rafts and floated them out to exhausted swimmers. They rescued others who jumped off their roofs into the river to grab onto a cotton bale and be pulled to safety on the banks.

Villagers fought the river with their own hands and feet. As the hours slowly moved, pitiful cries for help became weaker.

Reaching out to her daughter with so many questions in her face, Mandy asked, "What has happened? I can't puzzle it out."

"The river exploded, Momma, and almost carried us with it!"

* * *

Amanda Rebecca and John Petty raised six children. Their sons and daughters started work in the mills at the early ages of eight and nine. School was not a priority to mill families that needed every penny to make ends meet. Julie and Eula stood on boxes to place the empty perns on the spindles. Amanda stood beside them, modelling that job for her girls, as well as keeping those small hands from having an accident. The two generations labored in the upstate mills of Clifton, Pacolet, and Cowpens.

JULIE

"Be back directly, Tom," Julie Petty hollered into the house.

The weary wife shut the front door.

Locking it was unnecessary; no one secured their homes in the mill village of Cowpens, South Carolina, in 1939.

Julie knew Tom didn't notice her good-by. He missed so much, and not being able to hear isolated him. So often, she wished there was a contraption to help her husband perceive sounds again. If there were flying machines invented to fight a war, one of those smart scientists surely could create a much smaller device to amplify normal sounds. When Tom turned the radio volume up, Julie had to escape the deafening noise.

Just last year, in October of '38, Julie remembered how their neighbors sat and listened to that crazy actor scare half the country to death with his reading of *The War of the Worlds.* Sitting right next to their Philco radio on the kitchen table with the round button turned as far as it could go, Tom hung on to every word. She sat outside with their friends, the Hatchett and Thornton families, and they heard the chilling report of the Martian invasion loud and clear.

Inside the four-room house, Thomas Emory now nodded in his chair beside the stove. His father's two canes lay beside him. On the table was a clean orange ashtray, his tin of Sir Walter Raleigh's tobacco, and a cup of strong Cuban coffee. Julie bought the coffee at Dr. Till's Drugstore; it was a special order, carried only for her veteran husband.

She left Tom dressed in his daily attire of worn, but mended, brown pants; khaki button-in suspenders; and an ironed white shirt with the sleeves rolled up. Black garters held up his sagging socks. To keep his ankles from swelling, Julie loosely tied his high-top brogans.

A red shawl hung lightly around his shoulders, and a tattered brown quilt covered his lap and legs. His well-worn family Bible lay on a stool on the other side of the rocker. The porcelain thunder mug was within reach, so he didn't have to walk outside to the outhouse. Some of the houses had indoor bathrooms added on to the back of their houses, but the Emorys didn't.

The closing door made him jerk, but his eyes didn't open. His years in battle caused him to easily startle, but he regained his composure just as quickly.

The Battle of Manila Bay left him a disabled veteran with hearing loss in one ear, damaged sight, and crippled legs. When his wooden frigate, the *USS Franklin*, exploded under him because of enemy fire, a long splinter damaged the nerves in his back. Tom had to learn to walk again, first with crutches and then with canes.

Not waiting for any response, the forty-seven-year-old Julie idly rubbed her temple and brushed back her light-brown hair, flecked liberally with white. In the same movement, she accidentally pushed her gold wire-rimmed spectacles off her nose, but not her face. Julie automatically straightened them and then stumbled on a loose board.

Narrowing her blue eyes in exasperation at her own clumsiness, she straightened herself and stood still for a moment. Noting the awkward start to her day, Julie said a brief prayer of thanks for not falling.

Then she crossed the narrow porch to the post and lightly patted it twice.

Julie's momma always touched the right porch post of their home whenever she left. Whether she was only on her way to her garden around the corner or off on a longer journey by wagon, Amanda Mosely Petty never forgot this patting ritual. When asked why she did it, Mandy simply smiled and replied, "My home needs all the blessings it can get."

Julie had followed her momma's example in this gesture of blessing her own home for thirty years. It was a ritual that was full of heartfelt significance.

Walking gingerly down the squeaking wooden steps to the small front yard, Julie wondered if the grass would rise again this year. Tom could not afford to buy new seed last fall, and the clay was only splotchy with minuscule green patches now. A few onions marked the front lawn.

With an effort, Julie straightened and stretched both her back and her resolve for the work day ahead. Admitting she was plumb tired was the honest-to-goodness truth.

Reaching the dirt road of Park Street, she bypassed the potholes made by the winter rains and snow. The holes were close enough to skip rocks up the street. The neighboring children were avid, afternoon competitors in this game. At least there were no puddles today to avoid; sunny days and spring winds had replaced the water with mud.

Her road accepted its morning once-over from the rising sun. Looking beyond the pecan trees, Julie could see the moon searching for its well-timed sanctuary in the distance. This familiar scene in the heavens never became old to her; she was fascinated by its repetitive uniqueness.

Tugging her brown knitted scarf and much-mended green sweater tighter, Julie briskly stepped up the simple slope to Linda Street. Today her faded cotton print dress matched the sweater.

Julie owned few dresses. She had three cotton dresses for work in the mill and one dress for church. She cut and stitched her own clothes. Her colorful short-sleeved work dresses were fashioned from the washed flour sacks bought at the mill store. Her black Sunday dress was long sleeved and ordinary; she had worn the same black felt hat for sixteen years. Two pairs of shoes, one pair of white gloves, three pairs of white socks and mended stockings, and a worn coat completed her wardrobe.

With both their clothes, the single undersized closet in their home was not crowded.

She knew a level sidewalk, not a dirt road, awaited her. The Cowpens Mill was then only a half a mile away. Most days, walking back and fro from work was a pleasure.

Gazing toward the top of the hill, her blue eyes sought the yellow bells and daffodils in her sister's front yard. Eula had loved those bright, golden colors since she was a child. Late March in South Carolina was their season to stretch and grow, and Eula excitedly shared daily reports of the flowers' progress to her friends at the mill.

And then Julie saw Eula there, waving her morning howdy, under one of the tall pecan trees in her yard. She paused to wait for Julie's own gesture and then slowly walked on. After Eula's twelve-hour shift of standing at the loom, daily chores now awaited her. There was breakfast to cook, chickens to feed, cows to milk, and the household to tidy.

Eula worked the night shift at the mill, so during the week, the sisters saw little of each other. Home duties and sleep pocketed their spare time, except on the weekends. Though the two families didn't live in the mill village, they lived mill lives. The shrill whistle of Cowpens Mill charted their days.

Julie patted both packed pockets of her apron. Yes, her scissors stuck out of the right side; they were in the leather sheath she had stitched. Without her scissors, she could not cut the slubs of knotted thread and tie off the ends of the thread. At the bottom of the other pouch were her two hankies, a yellow box of Checkerberry snuff, and a wooden brush to clean her teeth. Two sandwiches and a small apple were in the paper poke on top.

Today she and Tom were having peanut butter sandwiches again; his sat on the kitchen table waiting until he was hungry. She wrapped her two in waxed paper to keep the lint off them at the mill. A butter sandwich, with a little of her homemade strawberry jelly, was another yummy favorite. Julie wondered how that peanut butter would taste with her homemade jelly. It would be worth a try. Smiling, she looked forward to tomorrow's peanut butter and jelly sandwiches.

They both liked the new Peter Pan peanut butter, and they weren't by themselves. Because it was popular with many families, the company store ran out of its supply every week. Whole families were enamored with the new peanut paste that was sold in a tin can. A smiling girl, dressed in a dark green dress and pointed hat like one of those Irish leprechauns, decorated the side of the can.

Unexpectedly, head pain halted Julie in midstride; it quickly disappeared in seconds. It left her vision hazy, and she felt a little nauseated, as if she hadn't eaten breakfast. By this time, she was on the sidewalk of Linda Street. Julie leaned against the fence in front of the Hatchette's house and shook her head slightly. Closing her eyes from the sun's glimmers through the trees, Julie started humming one of her favorite hymns. Without thought, the resolute woman added the words to "Will the Circle Be Unbroken" as she tottered on. Her rhythmic steps matched the words.

There are loved ones in the glory,
Whose dear forms you often miss;
When you close your earthly story,
Will you join them in their bliss?

Will the circle be unbroken
By and by, by and by?—
In a better home awaiting
In the sky, in the sky.

In the joyous days of childhood,
Oft they told of wondrous love,
Pointed to the dying Savior;
Now they dwell with Him above.

You remember songs of heaven
Which you sang with childish voice,
Do you love the hymns they taught you,
Or are songs of earth your choice?

You can picture happy gath'rings
'Round the fireside long ago,
And you think of tearful partings,
When they left you here below.

One by one their seats were emptied,
One by one they went away;
Here the circle has been broken—Will it be complete one day?

The hymn reminded Julie of Iris's funeral. Walking to the funeral, the congregation sang those encouraging words. Julie and Tom's daughter Iris was only three when she died of whooping cough. That winter there were seven little ones in their church who passed on with that sickness; all of the children were under the age of five.

Remembering back to those long, two weeks in January, Julie was certain that Iris only had a bad cold in the beginning. When the dry cough turned into a coughing fit the first time, the nervous mother knew something else had gripped her small girl.

One morning, after ten days of sneezing and a runny nose, the coughing lasted so long that Iris turned red and then blue in her face. When she finally quit coughing, she made a small whooping sound. That sound was terrifying, and both mother and child caught their breaths in surprise.

Dr. Till had no medicine that would help the sick child. He told Julie to keep her warm, quiet, and full of fluids. Iris would just lie cuddled up in her bedcovers and hold her rag doll; she didn't even want to get up to play. Drinking fluids, as the doctor also ordered, often made little Iris cough and choke. Fear was in the child's eyes when she had a coughing spell, and Julie felt that same terror in her heart.

Coughing finally wore out Iris's little body.

Losing Iris still haunted Julie. A parent shouldn't have to bury a child; it was against nature. It was a living nightmare.

Even though whooping cough was extremely contagious, their other daughter, five-year-old Lois, was spared battling the disease. One of their neighbors lost two children that winter; that kind of suffering was mindboggling to Julie then and now.

Stopping and taking another deep breath, she realized the headache had disappeared. Julie blinked her eyes to check her vision, and all was clear. It was like the alarm never happened, so she headed on down the sidewalk once again.

The never-relenting black smoke from the burning coal coming from the smokestack beckoned her toward the mill. Honeysuckle vines were profuse with their flowers and the strong, sweet odor tempted Julie to stop for a sampling. She did not tarry this time.

Passing the vacant lot, she turned toward her younger sister Lovey's house. Lovey, Eula, and Julie all worked in the spinning room, but their shifts were never at the same time. Their sister Dovey was a spinner at Clifton Mill.

Lovey and Rosemond Coleman's house bordered the mill fence. Their home was a single-family dwelling, because it once was a mill supervisor's house. It was the only mill house on Linda Street; the rest of the mill village was back on the other side of the mill and went down Santee Street to the Daniel Morgan Cemetery.

Though there was no one in sight, Julie still called mornin' and waved. She was sorry that Lovey didn't run out, because she was always talking, as did her twin, Dovey. In fact, they often spoke at the same time; they never waited until the other one finished to start chatting either. From their childhood, they were double the fun, as well as being trickster look-alikes.

Each sister had dropped out of school in the third grade to join the rest of the family in working at the cotton mill. The hours were long, but paychecks were issued every week. Their parents, Amanda and John Petty, left their farm in Cherokee County and purposely moved to the mill village of Pacolet to save their children from starvation. Money from their crops could no longer pay their debts.

In the village built by the mill owners, the Petty family moved into a two-story house with another family. The house was divided down the middle by a wall, and each household had four rooms. The rent was two dollars per week. They began a new way of life of working in the mill together. By standing on boxes next to their mother, the Petty girls learned the spinning trade. Two generations, simultaneously and separately, labored together in a cotton mill, rather than in a field of cotton.

An iron fence surrounded the mill. The barrier stopped at the door of the stair tower. Julie looked up at the clock above the third floor and knew her delay had not made her late. She opened one side of the heavy wooden door, and the morning breeze helped her close it.

The spinning room was on the first floor, so she went straight ahead into the mill. Turning to the left, she walked to the water house and took a sip of water from the fountain. In the foyer were shelves and coat hooks. Julie chose a vacant peg to hang her sweater and scarf and placed her bag lunch on the shelf underneath.

Patting her hair to be sure all the metal bobby pins were tightly in place to keep any wisps of hair out of her eyes, Julie turned into the large and cavernous room that held the spinning frames. She squared her shoulders and methodically put one foot in front of the other.

The section man assigned the duties for each frame and kept the records for each shift. Each frame had two sides with an aisle or alley in between. A spinner worked the sides of two different frames.

Julie walked over to Jim Butler, the section man, who was dressed in his familiar attire of faded overalls covering his spindly legs and his patched, long-sleeved flannel shirt rolled up to the elbows."Mornin', Jim," Julie shouted. With the noise and his back to her, Julie knew it would be nigh impossible for him to hear her unless she yelled.

Jim quickly turned and nodded to Julie. Looking at his clipboard, he saw the next vacant spot.

Sunken circles under his eyes didn't keep him from grinning at Julie. When his wife Jennifer died, Julie and Tom had him to Sunday dinner for months. Their Christian charity never made him feel obliged.

"Howdy-do, Julie. Iris told me you women folk were gonna help out the Murphy family this weekend with a poundin'. I'm mighty proud to be a member of Central Baptist. Everyone helps their neighbors. Sad the way both husband and wife are down at the same time. Those three Murphy young'uns don't bring in much with their mill hours and wages."

"I don't rightly know how they could get along without our helpin'. I am baking two pans of my sodie biscuits this time and sharin' my last jar of strawberry jelly from last year. Hopin' it will go a long way to shorin' up a sweet tooth or two in that house."

"Dern tootin', you make the finest biscuits this side of the Mississippi!" Jim interrupted.

"Have a lot to be thankful for today, Julie." He nodded his head for emphasis.

"Sure no promises about havin' no troubles in this world in the Bible, but God'll help us through it all. My dad used to say if everything is comin' your way, you're on the wrong road!"

Jim assigned Julie to the frames on the far right side of the spinning room.

She followed Tom, a young sweeper, down her alley and knew the space would not be clean for long. The nine-year-old's knee pants and shirt were covered in lint. He pushed two straw brooms in front of him to shove balls of tangled thread, crumpled wax paper, and other trash away.

Soon that lint would cover her too. Town folks often called the mill workers lintheads. The slur *linthead* was apt in reality, but demeaning nevertheless.

The noisy, dusty, and humid room was an unhealthy environment, but it was the only workplace Julie had known since she was eight. To keep the threads from breaking, water sprayed from the ceiling in narrow hoses. The windows were never opened. Machine belts made slapping noises, and thousands of spinning bobbins whirred in the background. Keeping a hankie in easy reach for cleaning her nose and throat was second nature now. To be sure not to inhale too much lint, Julie never took a deep breath. Daily the damp and sticky air soaked through her clothes.

Shadows peered around the looms on the wooden floors. Thirty green enamel shades surrounding 200-watt bulbs hung

Spinners in the Cowpens Mill

from the ceiling and were the source for the pale light.

Sometimes it was difficult to remember back to those early years thirty-seven years ago. The skinny auburn-haired girl, afraid of the dark and her own shadow, had matured into a woman who was a right good spinner and fit as a fiddle. Her third grade education had not held her back.

Annie Mae waved at Julie from the alley they would share and work that day. The plump woman wore her green dress with the yellow flowers; its white collar was yellow from too many washings. She only had two work dresses, one blue and one green. Because her eyesight was failing, her glasses were thick. But after twenty-five years at her job, Annie Mae often proclaimed she could work blindfolded.

"I heard tell we would get to visit some today. Been wantin' to ask you about how Tom is farin'."

Smiling, Julie, took out her box of snuff. "He's gettin' by pretty well this week. Left him dozing in his chair and snug as a bug in a rug."

She got a pinch of her snuff, put it between her gum and cheek, and continued talking.

"I figure warm weather and my garden will spry him up for the summer. The cold weather saps him dry, and it was a long winter. Shorely blessed that he's seldom ornery."

"Julie, you're a long-sufferin' woman, for sure. Almost every day, my man hears the threat 'I'm gonna knock you into next week.'"

Annie Mae patted her friend's arm. "Don't be fergittin' it's my day to buy our Cokes from the dope wagon."

The dope wagon was a store on wheels. It always carried homemade sandwiches, candy bars, crackers, cigarettes, and headache powders. The most popular were the ice-cold dopes, the caffeinated beverages in a bottle. Those Coca-Colas were kept in a box filled with ice, and they were a pick-me-up that everyone looked forward to.

Both women turned toward their frames and their twelve-hour day. Already a sheen of cotton lint covered their clothes.

Their jobs were only part of the process that moved cotton through production that ended in a bolt of cloth. Beginning in the opening room, there were workers who untied the bales of raw cotton. An opening machine then fluffed up and cleaned that compressed cotton. Next were the lappers or pickers that smoothed the cotton into sheets, and then the card hands fed the sheets into carding machines that continued the cleaning of the loose cotton. This mass left the carding machine as a rope.

Julie and Annie Mae worked on the rope by putting up ends. Four or more ropes went through a roller at the head of a drawing frame. A machine combined all four into one rope. Tighter and tighter they were wound until they became a single thread. Doffers took the full bobbins off and replaced them. As the rope filled the bobbins, the two friends repaired any breaks or snags.

There was a rhythm to this mind-numbing task; these experienced women moved from one bobbin to another. Their eyes guided their hands and feet.

Bending over to work on the bottom row of bobbins hurt Julie's shoulders every day. Taking a BC Powder was not as effective as it used to be.

Leaning over, Julie gasped and grabbed the temples of her head. A searing pain knocked her to the lint-covered floor. Her brown horn-rimmed glasses broke in pieces. She screamed, and her voice was unrecognizable. There was terror, as well as pain, in her face, and she writhed on the floor.

Annie Mae ran to Julie and lifted her head off the floor into her lap. From down the alley, Lizzie heard the shrieks and also threw her scissors down and raced for the fallen woman. Soon Julie's shrieks were silent as she lost consciousness.

"Let's tote her outside to the well," ordered Jim, and he grabbed her feet.

Annie Mae picked up her right shoulder, and Lizzie her left. Only five feet and four inches, the slight woman was not heavy.

"Need you to skedaddle back to work." He nodded to the others, who had come to help. "Reckin I will get news back to you shortly."

Jim started walking backwards toward to the outside door; it wasn't far to the artesian well.

Julie was limp. Her eyes were still closed, but her body kept twitching.

Walking out into the spring morning was a welcome relief from the humid warehouse. The light breeze caressed Julie's face, but she didn't notice. Though sunlight dusted her eye lids, they didn't unwrap.

The three gingerly laid Julie down beside the well in the courtyard. No one was there to eat lunch yet.

Annie Mae dipped her yellow handkerchief in the well bucket and stroked Julie's face; there was still no response.

"Julie, Julie," Annie Mae whispered and then cautiously shook her friend's shoulders.

All three hovered over the quiet woman and waited for Julie to open her eyes. Their expressions were hopeful, yet full of fear.

Julie sighed and then stopped breathing.

She was free.

* * *

Julie Petty was born in Pacolet on April 12, 1886. She enjoyed sewing and doing handwork; quilting and stitching seat covers were her favorites. With the poor lighting in the mill houses, she depended on her spectacles. (John treasures one pair of his grandmother's glasses.) She lived through two world wars and the Great Depression, never faltering in living one day at a time.

Julie and Tom are buried in Thompson's Chapel Cemetery on the banks of the Pacolet River.

LIZZIE

Lizzie Ingle closed her eyes again, but sleep continued to evade her weary body.

Three o'clock was too early to be getting out of bed; the long-legged brunette could have slept about an hour longer, but she was wide awake. The rooster was not even making its familiar morning squawks from the pen in the backyard. Her husband continued to snore with his usual gusto.

Just as the wagon ride from Green Knob Mountain had shaken their bodies around those mountain curves last week, thoughts and fears had rattled Lizzie's consciousness all night. In fact, the past two weeks had been unsettling from start to finish.

Lizzie began to play back the days in her mind.

Her thirty-six-year-old husband, Make Ingle, and his brothers owned a pulpwood business. Fair weather was vital to their partnership. Blaine, Frank, Isaac, and Make, the four brothers, worked year-round to support their families. They owned two wagons with teams of mules and made deliveries to the Chesapeake and Ohio Railroad every other day. Then the railroad cars moved the wood to Champion Mill in Canton, North Carolina.

Green Knob Mountain was between Flag Pond and Erwin, Tennessee, in the middle of the Appalachian Mountains. Their house was near the top, and Lizzie was proud of those four rooms. There were windows on all sides, and the painted skies at sunrise and sunset thrilled her soul.

It was a natural forest with thickets of wild blueberries and blackberries, rhododendrons, and mountain laurel. Besides these lush plants, there was an abundance of trees. Fraser fir and red spruce were the two species the Ingles cut most.

Monday, Wednesday, and Friday were their transport days; they felled the trees each day, except Sunday. The siblings needed a day of rest on the Sabbath; cutting, trimming, and hauling trees were demanding work. Accidents were more numerous if fatigue was a factor, because it led to carelessness.

The men and their sons, who were the work crew, deftly labored together to produce each full truck. Ten-year-old Oscar and eight-year-old Harvey were Make's oldest children. Even though they were young, the two could cut the logs with a crosscut saw to fit in the eight-foot wagon. There was much competition between these two brothers.

This 1915 winter was abundant with snow. Each week, the inches built up, and then came the torrential spring rains. Makeshift log bridges washed away; the mud converted to a deep and sloshy jam on the dirt roads and trails that circled the hills. Spring planting was postponed again and again.

Make could ordinarily make ends meet for his household with odd jobs, but the weather had thwarted all prospects for making extra money. Rebuilding fences, replacing stones in chimneys, and fixing leaking roofs were all impossible because of the weather. Rain was a fact of life in this mountainous area, but this year a daily deluge had been the pattern.

Week by week, twenty-nine-year-old Lizzie watched her husband's frustration grow. They had been married for eleven years, and she knew his moods well. He continued to fix what he could around the house and barn. All the knives he used for butchering and axes for cutting wood had been sharpened. He mended plows, tack for the horses, and the two water troughs. Dropping tobacco from his pipe every few minutes, he repaired the patched steps to the second floor. Nervous energy kept him primed for the next task.

Lizzie's brow furrowed as she thought back to the evening they talked about the inevitable move.

In late April, only two weeks ago, Lizzie and Make sat down to discuss their options. They made themselves comfortable in the caned chairs that Make had fashioned as a present to mark their first anniversary.

Before he spoke, Make methodically stoked his pipe.

"Sweetheart, I reckin I'm 'bout to my wits end and don't know which way to turn." He shook his head in bewilderment. "This here weather has pert-near got the best o' me and our future."

Lizzie was squinting to mend the socks in her lap. There were several pairs that needed her attention. Her glasses were on the mantel, but she didn't want to get them. She had impatiently waited for this opportunity to see what he had in his mind. Early in their marriage, she had learned that no good consequences came from harping at Make. She laid the socks aside.

Make started again. "Me 'n Isaac 'n Blaine got together at Frank's yesterd'y to see what we could figger out. We overhauled the wagons. Replaced some broken boards in the bed, 'n fixed one of the axles, 'n greased all the wheels. Sharp'n'd ever' saw 'n ax."

"None of us has been sick with the flu n'r pneumonia this year. We're as fit as fiddles! But we can't work."

"My ma tole' me once't that Unicoi means 'fog draped,'" said Lizzie. "Unicoi County is slap lost in a cloud this year, Make. This weather's fogged in the whole of this mountain, n' it's a plumb misery." She shook her head. "The Good Book tells us not to fret, but I confess I've been a'frettin'."

Lizzie reached around to rub her back. She was pregnant with their fifth child; July was her due date, and that was only three months away. Annie Mae was six and Jenny five. During this pregnancy, Lizzie had experienced a lot of back pain, and she had needed her daughters. The two girls were excited about a new baby and were willing to do chores. Since Jenny was born, Lizzie had lost three babies. She and Make were thrilled about this child.

In vexation, Make reached up with both hands to scratch his head. The action mirrored his thoughts.

Then he stood up and paced.

"When me n' the boys were feeding the horses and cows t'other day, Oscar and Harvey started talkin' agin about those *Boy's Life* magazines I bought fer 'em. Who would have thought magazines would be popular with my boys?"

The proud father raised his chin a little higher, reflecting on his third grade education. He wanted more for all his children.

"I remember standin' there in Erwin's hardware store lookin' at the magazine covers and soundin' out the words 'stories of adventure and darin'.' That story of the blind scouts and what they could do even now teches me. Oscar and Harvey still a'carry those beat-up compasses they made out of scraps last year around in their overall pockets. Lizzie, they lernt how jist from readin'."

He pointed his finger toward the bedroom where his children slept. "That twenty cents for magazines was dern well spent.

I wonder where they would have gotten their schoolin' iffen Miz Jennie Moore hadn't decided to come to these here mountains. She has lernt my boys. And jist think: I heped cut down the trees thet built Rocky Fork Community Center. I'm terrible proud of that."

Lizzie smiled.

Make smiled back. "I don't hev' the book smarts you have, sweetheart. I could never hep' start a college like yer brothers Harrison and Lee did. In my part of the hills, Forks of Ivy, nev'r had nary a school when I's a'comin' along. The folks taught us to figger a bit and write our names. The onliest book we had was the Bible. Papa said it was the onliest book we'd ever need to read. Some of them words are mighty long."

"Lizzie," he rambled on, "I can't rightly say jus' what I mean, but I want our young'uns to have more'n we had. This hilly ground is 'bout wore out for planting. All this rain's gonna put a blight on our corn and tobak'r. We didn't git to plant the garden on Good Friday, and this rain is looking like we might need to build an ark, rather'n sow seeds!"

Weariness and defeat etched each of his sentences.

"We got to . . ." Make halted.

His finished sentence was life changing.

"Leave these hyer mountains and go south. Me n' the boys can git jobs in one of them cotton mills whar' we c'n make a paycheck ev'r week. The mills hev' got rental houses n' they hire school teachers and doctors. It's a village. You'll have neighbor wimen to talk to n' we c'n walk to church."

Lizzie looked into his eyes.

"Sweetheart, say somethin'. Are you with me? I know we c'n do it together.

I figger we c'n sell what we can't take with us. That c'n git us started. Isaac 'n Blaine'l buy one of my wagons and stock. Our cabin'l git us a pretty good penny. I can't imagine us leaving our place here. I hate it like the dickens. This home and land are our'n, n' it sorely hurts my heart to leave it. But we got to git ahead, n' then we can move ourselves back to these beautiful mountains."

Though strained with emotion, Make's voice ended with a slight hope in the future.

"Ever since thet comp'ny man come around t'other week from thet Tucapau Mill tellin' us they wuz a'hirin', I been a' considering thet this here's the best thang t'do. I like it thet we'd be hepin' the war over in Europe. South C'lina ain't too far thet we can't come back to visit." He paused.

"Lizzie, you still ain't said nuthin'. Talk to me."

"Lordamercy, Make! I don't know when I'da put in a word. You ain't stopped long a'nuff to take a breath! Shore, I reckon we'll go to South C'lina."

She lifted herself out of the chair, walked to her husband, and put her arms around his neck.

"I mind our wedding vows said 'fer better 'r fer worse,' and we've seen both. A move might be just the ticket. This here winter and sprang has slap-dab wore me out. I love you, Harvey Maken Ingle, and don't you ne'er fergit it."

Within ten days, Lizzie and Make had either sold, given away, or packed up their household. Both their families had helped. Each day was like a family reunion on Green Knob Mountain. Most of the talk was of remembrances, since no one wanted to dwell on them leaving. Their working together proved true that many hands made light work. As the pile to give away grew twice as tall as the pile of takes, Lizzie truly saw what this moving was requiring of her. She kept giving slices of her heart away to someone else.

Each night the families gathered in Make's barn. Sawhorse tables filled quickly with ham, fried chicken, vegetables of all kinds, plus biscuits, cornbread, and plenty of desserts. Some of the men gathered around the glass jars of homebrew, and the children ran wild with their games.

Lizzie plucked her dulcimer. Isaac and Blain kept time with their fiddles. A neighbor played his banjo. The songs were loud. Children and adults clogged, and the wood floor quivered. Some only hummed and clapped; no one was silent.

"Sourwood Mountain," "Turkey in the Straw," and "Little Brown Jug" were performed several times each night. They were obvious favorites from the exuberant playing and singing.

The children belted out the chorus of "Little Brown Jug" to the top of their lungs. Their laughs often turned into foolish giggles with the chorus.

Ha, ha, ha, you and me,
Little brown jug, don't I love thee!
Ha, ha, ha, you and me,
Little brown jug, don't I love thee!

When the mournful ballads were played, rather than the hoe-down songs, the singing had a reverence about it. "Barbara Allen" was the most requested. The first line always quieted the crowd.

In Scarlet Town where I was born
There was a fair maid dwelling
Made every youth cry 'Well-a-day'
Her name was Barbara Allen.

Awakening in a strange house in another state, Lizzie softly cried, stuffing her hand in her mouth, not wanting to wake her husband. She covered her head with the quilt, thinking of the family they left behind.

Make and his brothers had packed the large wagon. Rather than moving trees, this time it would carry a family's household. There was room for the coops of chickens and the few pieces of their worn furniture. They had piled the truck high with the children's two sleeping pallets, their parents' bed and mattress, Lizzie's rocking chair, the two caned chairs, a butter churn, an iron wash pot, and their kitchen table and benches. In between were linens, clothes, pots, dishes, and what was left of the canning from last summer.

Leftover onions, apples, Irish potatoes, and sweet potatoes from the stone well house were stored in homemade hemp sacks. Corn, beans, okra, peanuts, tomato, squash, and watermelon seeds were in small handmade sacks for a new garden. A few leftovers from the pantry were added at the last minute.

Inside the pillow cases were Make's tools for woodworking, and Lizzie's dulcimer was wrapped in a quilt rolled up in between the folded mattress. At last, there were no small holes or gaps to stuff. They tied rope over and around the wagon bed until it was wrapped like a package.

The cows' mournful mooing that final morning echoed the family's silent words. The clan shared final hugs, as well as tears, as the eager Ingle children jumped around. Between the generations was a lack of awareness; each was in their own separate world.

Squashed together on the buckboard seat were the girls and their parents; the two boys barely had room for their bottoms in the bed of the wagon. The seven-months-pregnant Lizzie had little space to spare. Jenny was the first to sit in her daddy's lap as he drove. The others would have their turns.

Pulling out as the sun came up behind the mountains was a view to remember. It was a welcome sight for the beginning of their trek.

Lizzie had reached and held her two girls tight when Make drove past the family cemetery where their three babies were buried. She choked down sobs but couldn't hold back the tears. Make reached over to grab her hand. So his wife would not miss every possible glimpse of the tiny rocks that covered the three small graves, Make slowed the wagon and mules again.

The journey took about three days. From the first rays of light until dusk, they moved further from home. Each night, they cuddled together under the wagon to sleep. They followed the dirt roads through Asheville, Hendersonville, Tryon, Saluda, Landrum, and

Spartanburg. Stopping to let the mules rest and the children run was part of the day. On the steep grade down the Saluda Mountain, Make had to pull the brake up over and over to stay on the road and not go over the side of the mountain.

Finally they crossed the railroad tracks of Tucapau Station #4129 for the Southern Railroad. This was where the raw cotton from the fields came in and where the finished products from the mills were also shipped out.

Slowly the wagon moved along Chestnut Street, and the family saw the Tucapau Baptist Church. Lizzie pointed out another steeple, but they couldn't tell the denomination. Cookie-cutter houses lined each road. Within easy walking distance were a school, a community building, and the company store.

When the four-story Tucapau Mill with the pointed roof of the belfry rising above it came into view, its size shocked Lizzie and Make. The red brick building was massive. From the smokestack wafted smoke from the boiler room. Their children pointed with animated gestures and voices to this huge structure on the banks of the Middle Tyger River.

As the couple looked at all the extraordinary sights, they began to grasp some of the magnitude of how their lives were going to change.

Lizzie and Make heard the mill whistle blow, but knew nothing of its significance. It signaled that for some of the workers at Tucapau Mill their ten-hour work day was finally over. A mill whistle chartered and controlled the mill workers.

As the mules moseyed along, the community waved a welcome. Many added a smile and howdy. Finally Make pulled on the reins and then the brake in front of a white house with a chimney. Taking a deep breath, he reached over to Lizzie.

"Welcome home, sweetheart! Welcome home!"

The children started climbing out and ran to the front porch. Finding the front door unlocked, the four raced in. Make helped Lizzie down, and the two stood intently looked at 4 Pine Street.

As they walked by and saw the loaded wagon, new friends, who had just gotten off work, put their lunch buckets down and started helping unload. They exchanged names with handshakes and made short work of placing it all inside.

Lizzie's rag rugs were positioned in every room. One of their new neighbors placed a Mason jar of blue irises on top of the oilcloth tablecloth. Before long there was a pot of beans and corn pone for their supper. One lady came over with a half dozen eggs. No one came empty-handed, and the adults' welcomes were sincere. Their neighbors showered them with hospitality.

Lizzie and Make were overwhelmed.

A seven-year-old boy named Jimmy Jordan wandered over and quickly made friends with Oscar and Harvey. The three started a game of catch that would become a daily pastime for the boys for many years.

Four little girls from next door took Annie Mae and Jenny to their porch to play with their dolls. Lizzie had made her daughters' dolls from different scraps and made sure they had long yarn hair to pull back with ribbons. Introductions of their cloth dolls and an examination of their clothes kept the six in a circle until suppertime. Both the dolls and their owners passed inspection.

And now it was Monday, their first day of work at Tucapau Mill.

Lizzie pulled the quilt up around her shoulders. The covering was a wedding present, handmade by her mother. The pinks, blues, and greens of the design were cheerful, and Lizzie sought their joy. Neither she nor Make Ingle had ever worked in a mill before, and her apprehension was causing her heart to race. Her husband's hard sleeping was beyond her ken.

In midsnore, Make sputtered and then stretched his six-foot frame. He turned to his wife of eleven years and said good morning with a kiss. "Reckin we might sip on a cup of coffee, sweetheart?"

He then rolled over, pulled on his overalls from beside the bed, and headed for the outdoor privy.

With a smile, Lizzie rose and went to fill the enamel coffee pot with water and coffee. She stoked the embers in the fire box of the wood stove with a couple of pine knots and kindling. She checked the ash box to see if it needed emptying, but there was room for more ashes. Then she lit a few candles.

Walking back to their bedroom, she pulled on her print cotton dress and a bleached-white apron to cover some of the bulge of her pregnancy. A blue hand-knitted sweater completed her work ensemble. Slipping on her shoes and brushing her hair back from her face, Lizzie was ready for the day.

Realizing there was plenty of time to get breakfast started before waking the sleeping children, she decided to make flapjacks. They would be filling, and she knew the sorghum molasses would be tasty on top. Lizzie pulled out her cast-iron frying pan, greased it with butter from the ice box, and started making the batter.

She poured two cups of coffee and handed Make his when he came back in the door.

He sat down at the table and blew on the hot brew.

"I reckin we didn't sleep too well last night. I kept dreamin' I was fallin' off a cliff. Sorry about all my tossin', sweetheart. My brain danced around over the past two weeks last night. I jest couldn't turn it off. These flapjacks smothered in molasses will straighten us out for the day."

Lizzie turned three onto a plate, so Make could start eating while they were hot. She knew he didn't like cold food when it was supposed to be hot. She handed him breakfast.

"I'll have some more cooked for you shortly."

"Lizzie, in a couple of hours we are gonna be mill hands in a cotton mill in South C'lina. I can scarcely believe it. Fer shore, we are gonna be larning a new job. I want to larn it quick, so I can make a decent livin' fer us."

Make stopped to fill his mouth with flapjacks, then continued, "It's important that you take it easy, sweetheart. I know you're used to standing on your feet in the house doing your work, but this is gonna be different. Breaks are gonna be important. You need to pay a'fair amount of attention to you and the baby all the time."

"I know," Lizzie quietly responded, as she gave him three more pancakes. "I'm afeared too. This young'in was kicking to beat the band this morning, so I know the little darlin's agettin' a mite crowded."Make, did you see that precious girl next door? Her name is Peggy, and she has purty blonde hair. Her head is larger than normal, and there's not much light in her eyes. She just looks around absent-mind- like.

"Peggy came over with her momma, Sara Jane, yestiddy. While we's sittin' on the porch, Sara Jane told me that Peggy was seventeen, even though she looks a lot younger. She couldn't larn nuthin'out of books. But down ter th' mill, she tuk to spinnin'right off. Peggy larn'd faster'n enny of th' others.

"Me n' Peggy are mountain girls, but I do believe she is more strong jawed. Her husband got hurt in the mill, and now he's a cripple. But he still pulls his weight. He's got an ole horse and wagon, and he hauls coal, wood, or furniture. Peggy says he don't make much, but he gits out n' does the best he can ever' day."

Lizzie wiped her eyes with her apron hem. Then she sat down with her own cup of coffee and flapjacks.

Make asked the Lord's blessings on their food, children, and their neighbors.

"Lord in Heaven, make us truly thankful for these n' all Thy many blessin's. Bless this food to the nourishm't of our bodies and us to Thy service. We ask your blessin's on all who stand in need. In Jesus name, amen."

They sat in silence, hearts going out to their new neighbors, and both began to think of ways they could lessen the loads next door.

It wasn't long before the morning craziness of the family commenced. Four sleepy children arose, and the smells from the kitchen drew them away from their pallets. Lizzie had put a platter of flapjacks in the stove's warmer for them, and their quiet turned to excitement over the molasses.

Lizzie quickly made bologna sandwiches for their lunch. One of their new neighbors had brought it from the company store, and the homemade bread was from someone else. She made two sandwiches for Make. They had leftover cake from the pounding, so Lizzie put a slice of that in to celebrate their first day at a new school and a new job. She wrapped it all in clean cloths. The children had pokes, and the adults would carry lunch pails.

The parents led the way out the door, and the children looked like small clones walking behind them. Annie Mae and Jenny's dresses were made from the same bolt of cloth as Lizzie's, and the boys sported overalls like Make.

As they walked toward the school, they were joined by other parents and their children. It was a long parade by the time they reached the school.

The first Monday whistle blew, as Lizzie and Make crossed the bridge over the river with all the rest of the workers. They saw the two dams that controlled the water that ran the mill on the Tyger River and created Berry's Pond. It was a stunning and clear river, and the falls created a soothing sound of water tumbling.

This identical walk to the mill would be repeated over and over, but never again without the knowledge of the struggle and work that would be required inside.

Lizzie cradled her pregnant belly and walked into the yawning door of Tucapau Mill.

* * *

Born in 1885 in Unicoi County, Tennessee, Artie Elizabeth Horne Ingle died on her sofa of a cerebral hemorrhage in 1939.

Lizzie married at age sixteen on September 1, 1900; she and Make had seven sons and three daughters. About 1923, the family moved to another mill village in Union, South Carolina, and Make worked as a night watchman at Union Mills. Lizzie became a busy homemaker in a two-story, eight-room house on 14 Lawson Avenue. They joined the Green Street Methodist Church.

EULA

I've got a home in glory land that outshines the sun.
I've got a home in glory land that outshines the sun.
I've got a home in glory land that outshines the sun.
Way beyond the blue.

Do Lord, O, do Lord, O do remember me.
Do Lord, O, do Lord, O do remember me.
Do Lord, O, do Lord, O do remember me.
Way beyond the blue.

I took Jesus as my Savior, you take Him too.
I took Jesus as my Savior, you take Him too.
I took Jesus as my Savior, you take Him too.
Way beyond the blue.

Do Lord, O, do Lord, O do remember me.
Do Lord, O, do Lord, O do remember me.
Do Lord, O, do Lord, O do remember me.
Way beyond the blue.

I take Jesus as my Savior, you take Him too.
I take Jesus as my Savior, you take Him too.
I take Jesus as my Savior, you take Him too,
While He's calling you.

The women's voices slowly softened, but the porch rockers continued to sway.

Porch society had no gender or age requirements in the mill villages. Most houses had both a front and back porch. Tin roofs covered them both.

Eula Mae Petty's back porch was a utilitarian one. At the top of the three steps was a wooden brush nailed to the floor. Eula didn't like dirty floors and expected guests to use it. Hanging by nails on the outside wall were a hoe, garden rake, and mop.

On either side of the porch posts were low shelves to support her two #22 wash tubs, one for washing and one for rinsing. The washboard was in easy reach. Buckets were at ready for the short trek to the water pump at the well to fill the tubs. When not in use, all the paraphernalia for washing also decorated the outside wall.

Over to the side was Eula's drying rack. Attached to the rectangular, wooden frame was screen wire to lay the fruit and vegetables on. The terra-cotta pots, neatly stacked by size, sat organized for the next planting.

The front porch had its own atmosphere of friendliness and "set a spell" invitations. Whether a visit was purposeful or not, a guest was always welcome. Because all the mill houses faced the streets and everyone knew everyone, there was no alarm to a casual visit.

This mill community was friendly and inclined to share their free time with family and friends. Front porches offered a sanctuary and welcome to all that climbed the steps.

Eula's metal glider and chairs were arranged for conversation. A quiet creek accompanied the glider's movement, but it wasn't an annoying sound. There were three rocking chairs and a couple of wooden stools randomly placed.

Tobacco smells filled the air around the porches. Men smoked cigars and rolled their own cigarettes. Women dipped and spit snuff.

Standing up and walking to the railing to spit her dip, Eula commented to the others, "Reckin we didn't raise the roof with our vocalizin' like in the church house this mornin'. Only a few neighbors up the street joined us."

Chuckling, Eula picked up her needle and thread and sat back down to continue her task of sewing anther quilt block. Her older brother Frank was going to need a new covering by Christmas.

Frank lived in the front room of her house. It was sparsely furnished with a chaise lounge, dresser, and straight chair. There was a fireplace to help keep him warm. Eula had watched him shiver, as he sat right beside a blazing fire.

Frank had to sit up in the chaise lounge to sleep now. Two short mattresses created a soft bed. Since the back could be adjusted, these days he changed its slant often.

Lying down caused him to have shortness of breath and irregular breathing. Emphysema and brown lung disease tortured his lungs. His working days in the mill, as well as his smoking, caused the deterioration. The cotton dust blocked the lungs' airways, so he wheezed most of the time. His chronic cough drove them both crazy.

He ate little, because he would choke and then have to catch his breath. When Eula pounded on his back to help him, he would bob forward from the stress of the blow and almost fall on the floor. Frank was a sick man, and their doctor, Dr. Till Martin, had no more suggestions to help him.

Eula pushed her hair back up off her neck and refastened the bun with loose bobby pins. Her long hair fell below her waist, but she kept it out of her face and out of her way by pulling and twisting it up to her scalp.

During the 1920s, many younger women had cut their hair into new and trendy short bobs. This was a blunt cut that was level with the ear lobes all around the head. Its simplicity was drastic when compared to the favored long, feminine locks. Eula's generation still believed that short hair was too masculine a style for women.

With tortoise shell combs and bobby pins, the curls stayed in place. Bobby pins were a new invention, and Potter's Store on Main Street kept them in stock. Attached to paper cards or packaged in metal tins, no woman ever had enough. This small, double-pronged hair pin held the hair in place. Crafted of either metal or plastic, children discovered pins that had lost their rubber tips could become small and effective weapons.

Their usefulness expanded as the pins became book marks, small clothespins, or instruments to clean the wax out of ears. The daily sweeping of the house often included a few strays that had been lost. Wiping off the dust or dirt immediately made them salvageable.

Eula Petty, her older sister Julie Petty Emory, and their sister-in-law Ollie Emory Petty were both close neighbors and kin. Their Sunday afternoon visits were deliberate gatherings intended for catching up on the gossip of their Cowpens, South Carolina, mill world. This October 27, 1929, was no different, and they enjoyed the bright, afternoon sun.

Julie was a slight woman, but she was strong and energetic. Her positive attitude about life and God's purposes kept her looking toward the future and not looking at the harshness of her past. She was the first in her family to buy spectacles. The lens was made of small and round glass, and the rims were gold. Though the lenses were wimpy in strength and didn't help her eyesight enough, she was proud to wear them. They were a fashion statement.

Married to Julie and Eula's older brother Boyd, Ollie was dumpy, but she wasn't lazy. She often had a catch in her speech. It was like she was working on getting an extra breath. Her voice was high-pitched like her grandfather, High Key Mosely. She often complained about the troubles of finding a new place in her legs to give herself insulin shots. Diabetes was a disease that daily tested her, but she was good-natured about it.

Eula had a special place in her heart for Lois, Julie's only child, and was generous with her. She would pick up trinkets or a couple of pieces of lemon candy for the young girl, just because. Every other weekend, Eula made an egg custard pie, because it was Lois' favorite. Her tin pie plate was small, so they would divide the pie in quarters. The light crust filled with the sweet and creamy eggs, milk, and sugar mixture was easy to make and bake; it was the ground ginger that gave it an extra zing.

Lois was thirteen, and she was making chinaberry necklaces. At her age, there was little entertainment on Sundays, so she chose to listen to the meandering stories of these three women. Her auburn hair was braided, and her blue eyes intently studied life. Even though she was quiet, there was little she missed.

A chinaberry tree grew in Ollie's front yard. The berries fell to the ground every fall. Last month Lois picked baskets of berries, pushed the soft centers out, and laid them on top of feed sacks to dry out.

Heating crushed walnut hulls created a warm brown dye that the dried chinaberries soaked up. By controlling how long the berries stayed in the dye, the hues ran from beige to a chocolate brown. Drying the berries once again made fast the dye.

Stringing the berries was easy. Lois liked to combine different size berries, as well as shades, for her jewelry. She gave them as gifts to her friends and family.

Lois worked in the mill with her mother and aunt. When she turned ten, the Petty women invited her to join their Sunday get-togethers. Lois sat on the floor between her mother and Eula. The small porch was cozy with heart-to-heart talk and laughter.

"Momma, whar'd you learn to fix leather britches?" asked Lois.

When it came to finding out the particulars of cooking, baking, or sewing, the young girl had sundry questions.

Julie smiled. "Yer granny lernt me." Eula interrupted, "I's always the last to learn anything, cuz I's the youngist. When I's five, Ma started me to strangin' beans and crowder peas on a hot summer day. My fangers could hardly hold the bean in one hand n' the needle in the other."

Julie said, "Bein' four years older, Eula'd sit in my lap. I'd hold her hands steady-like. Thar hain't no talent to puttin' that needle threaded with string through that stem end. That's the only part of the pod strong enuff to hold it."

Ollie interrupted, "My ma learned me to put that needle in the middle of a bean. I thought they was purty like a necklace. Couldn' put but a couple of feet of them separated by an inch or two on that twine. It'd be too heavy, n' that strang'd shorely break."

Ollie pulled a light blanket up over her legs. Between diabetes and arthritis, she had a time out in the cooler weather. To even walk across the street to Eula's house, she used a long chinaberry stick for a staff.

Her system worked fair for short distances. She would reach forward with the staff, steady it on the ground, and then shuffle around it. Ollie was stout, and her extra weight hindered quick movements. Many repeats later, and she would collapse in one of Eula's rockers. Ollie's grit was evident.

Eula continued, "Lois, you know how I plumb love peaches. That's why I dry me some peaches in the summer on the back porch. I git my dryin' rack and then line peaches on the wire. They git covered with a ole sack to keep the yellow jackets and flies off 'em. When they dry, I string 'em.

Jist like those dried peaches hangin' in my kitchen, Momma hung them strangs of beans up on nails to dry. Then she stored them in an old dry sack until Pop hankered for some during the winter.

Ma'd stoke up the wood stove to boil water in her big iron pot. She always added soda to it afore she put the beans in. After the beans softened, she'd drain that water off."

Eula paused. Her reminiscing gave clear pictures to her mind's eye of her mother's simple cooking. She pushed a loose piece of brown hair back behind her right ear. Turning her cloth square to bind it on another side, she picked up the story. "Then Ma started again with clear water from the well, but this time those beans simmered with a chunk o' fatback." Then the conversation took another turn. "Heard tell Alice is feelin' poorly agin. If I'd been blessed with seven chillern, I might feel poorly all the time! Not even two years between the birthin's of most of them. That husband of hers needs to take a vacation."

Eula shook her head at what she had said aloud.

Born in 1890, Eula was single, but she was not a leftover blessing.

Tom Helms had swept her off her feet when she was seventeen. New to Cowpens Mill and the community, he moved into Mrs. Martin's Boarding House on the corner of Palmetto and Spring Streets. Eula was impressed with his manners to the women; he treated them like ladies. Before long, the two were eating lunch together at the well, and he made her giggle with his stories.

Working in the warehouse, he soon became known for his strength in hauling the warps to the weaving room. These awkward and heavy rolls of thread were delivered on a cart to the weaver at a loom. Tom would then pick up the warp by one end of the steel spindle that ran through the warp and place it on the rack on one side of the loom. Next he picked up the other end of the spindle and placed that end of the warp on the rack on the other side. The repetition of this job secured him a muscular physique.

Within a month, their courting ended with a wedding in the home of the pastor at Central Baptist Church of Cowpens. Neither were members, but the pastor pronounced them man and wife with blessings on their marriage. So in the sight of God and the witness of the pastor's wife, Eula became Mrs. Tom Helms. She moved into the boarding house with Tom.

While the other three women continued sharing gossip about family and neighbors, Eula stewed over how he had hoodwinked her.

Two weeks after their wedding, Tom came in late one Saturday night after a time out with some of the single men who lived there. As he stumbled up the stairs to their room, he lost his balance. Crashing into the wall with a loud curse, he crawled the rest of the way to their room. As he pushed the door open with his strong shoulder, the door strained against its hinges.

The stench of the liquor stunned Eula; she didn't know Tom drank. A sickening feeling enveloped her.

"You're snockered, Tom Helms!"

She hurried over to help him up, but he pushed her away with a growl.

"Thinkin' you be so high and mighty, Miss Euler. I got somethin' that might really give you a stir."

Startled at his words, as well as his condition, Eula plopped down in the straight chair in their room. She looked at him with trepidation; she did not know this Tom. Her heart pounded, and a flush turned her face hot. A sickening feeling turned her stomach.

With some effort, he staggered off the floor and lit a cigarette. The springs on their iron bed squeaked loudly, as he bounced once before gaining his balance.

"It's time for truth tellin'," he growled.

Shaking his head to unscramble his thoughts, he smiled at his bride.

"Yeah, I moved from Gaffney, like I tol' you. But I didn't tell you I lef' a wife and two babies there. I wanted to start over away from all 'em family things, so hyer we are. Them babies cried all the time. She couldn't make 'em quit, n' I'd enuff of it. So I lef' 'em in that there three-room house in Limestone mill village n' hiked over hyer."

Sitting in stunned silence, Eula's mind jumped from shock to fury. She bounded out of the chair, knocking it to the floor.

"You needn't to worry none," Tom continued, trying to pacify her. "I'm ain't gonna leave you! Jist thought I'd share a few particulars."

"Git outta this room, Tom Helms! You hain't got no right to be hyer. You hain't my husband, 'cause yer already hitched."

Rejection burned Eula's heart.

She sprang toward the shut door and opened it once again. With flashing eyes, she pointed to the stairs and shouted, "Git out, you two-faced varmint. Git outta here, liar and pretender! I'm a prayin' you git a taste of your own medicine."

Swaying as he walked, Tom edged toward the door. Frowning at Eula in disbelief, he crossed the threshold.

Believing he was moseying slowly to irritate her further, Eula threw his dusty valise out behind him. Then she grabbed up his clothes and started throwing them. This scorned woman clearly knew how to throw a duck fit.

She ignored his placating voice and words, "Now, hon', let's talk a bit. Simmer down. We can work this out."

Eula answered by tossing his razor and shaving cream out the door.

Mrs. Martin's loud voice interrupted their to-do.

"Mr. and Miz Helms, I afear your ruckus is too much. Youn'ses need to settle down. Mr. Helms, no cause fer ya to be too big for your britches. New sweethearts are lovin'. No more hollerin' in my house now. You need to straighten up and fly right!"

Clearly expecting silence to reign once again in her home, their landlady turned and walked back to her quiet room.

Talking to herself, the older woman mumbled, "You'uns skeered the livin' daylights outta me."

Shame soaked Eula's countenance as she watched Tom stuff his things into his luggage. Tears streamed down her face, and her humiliation caused her to shiver. She tightened her arms around her narrow waist as if to hide her dishonor.

Tom ignored her. He made no sense as he babbled to himself. To save his pride, he needed to get away from the boarding house before his buddies returned. He straightened his suspenders and placed his felt Stetson hat straight on his head. Small communities noticed details, and he knew the gossips would have a heyday with this tale. Keeping up appearances would perhaps quell some talk.

Tom Helms staggered down the steps and stumbled out the door; he never looked back.

Eula stared down the stairs for a long time. Then she turned back to her room, packed her bag, and moved back in with her parents that night.

It was a jar to relive this wretched event in her life on this lovely fall afternoon. This recollection could still make her catch her breath.

Furtively looking up at the others, she realized no one had noticed her consternation and distress. She was glad that she still had the ability to usually stay quiet when deeply distressed.

That night, twenty-two years ago, a fury took her over she never wanted to experience again.

Julie's laughter brought her sister back to the porch.

"Doctor Til' is still usin' those same encouragin' words when hepin' with a delivery. All the children and Lizzie's sisters were fret-tin' waitin' on the new baby. He jist kept sittin' at the table, drinkin' his coffee, and readin' the newspaper. Lookin' up at the anxious faces, he nodded and said, 'Don't look so worried; when the fruit gets ripe, the apple will fall.'" Julie chuckled. "Great day in the mornin'! I reckin he means well by sech foolishness."

Doctor Andrew Tillman Martin practiced family medicine in Cowpens. His office was in the back of the Cowpens Drug Store. Patients sat outside in straight caned chairs in front of a curtain, strung across the back wall until it was their turn to see the doctor. There were no private diagnoses, even though they were sometimes whispered to a patient.

A graduate of the South Carolina Medical College, he began practicing medicine in 1919 after he came home from the Great War. He was a kind man who never turned away a patient and never hesitated to make house calls when needed.

Whether his patients were in the mill village or the town, humans or animals, Doctor Til' was their doctor.

"Ollie, did Boyd tell you about that Carolina Clemson game on Thursday?" Eula asked. "It was the talk of the mill on Friday. How those men can git so stirred up over two teams running up and down a field is shore beyond me." Lois nodded. "They were swapping stories and lies after church services today to beat the band. Anybody would think playin' with a ball covered in pig skin was important in South Carolina! They was doin' all that poundin' on the back and jabbin' each uther the way men do."

"Those men been talkin' about Big Thursday for weeks. Whar on earth did that name come from? Those undefeated Tigers won agin this year. Guess they won braggin' rights over the Fightin' Gamecocks, even it were jist by one touchdown."

Eula shook her head in bewilderment. "Ev'n Frank, sick as he is, was all agog listenin' to Jim Brown's stories yesterdy about that game. And then Frank wanted to retell it to me at supper. I jist sat there with my brain in shut down, acting like his tale was spellbindin'."

All four women laughed, and silence reigned on the porch momentarily.

The Carolina-Clemson football game was played in Columbia, South Carolina. The thirty-four-year rivalry started in 1896, and it was a morning game, part of the entertainment in the week-long South Carolina State Fair. For one day named Big Thursday, businesses, companies, and state schools shut down to celebrate. Men and women dressed in their Sunday best, and picnic baskets on blankets adorned various tailgates. Clemson was a military college, and the cadets slept outside in tents before the game. The opposing passions on the football field carried over into the stands; it was an earsplitting event.

Another incident that became known as Black Thursday, with vaster ramifications than Big Thursday, turned most lives around in the United States on that same October day in 1929. The stock market took a major plunge and ushered in the Great Depression. News trickled down south of this demise in New York City, as did the aftershocks in Upstate mills, where wages and work had already tumbled.

The sitters on Eula's porch would soon understand the true meaning of "They ain't got nary none."

Four local residents organized Cowpens Manufacturing Company in 1889. It started with seventy-five employees. In the early 1900s, employee growth was at its highest with over three hundred employees. The railroad depot was an asset to the shipment of manufactured cotton, and farmers in the area grew cotton on their land to sell to the mill. In the yard of the mill itself, the plant was also cultivated. The cotton seed was planted, picked, ginned, combed, woven, and shipped in this one small area, and the town of Cowpens prospered.

In the 1920s, cotton mills ran into financial difficulties. There was an overproduction of the crop during World War I, and then the boll weevil attacked the fields. Devastation prevailed, and cotton prices dropped. Mill workers were laid off, and the mill owners increased the workload of those left. Overworked and underpaid workers could not feed their families.

Mills initiated the stretch-out system. They required workers to work longer hours for less wages; sometimes their work doubled. By 1929, some wages sunk to five dollars a week. In April, a strike for more pay, fewer hours, and dismissal of the stretch-out began in Gastonia, North Carolina, at the Loray Mill. Brandon Mill, Duck Mill, and Poinsett Mill in Greenville had workers strike within days of each other. Eighty-one spontaneous strikes happened in South Carolina during this year, as families became more desperate.

"I arter not worry about this winter, but I admit to bein' afeared of makin' ends meet," Eula said. "Knowin' the Good Lord will take care of His children and trustin' Him to do it during these worrisome times makes me a tad skittish."

"Sister, now wait jist a cotton pickin' minute," Julie said. "Our ma used to say, 'The early bird gits the worm,' and she trained us to do jist that. There was no lollygagglin' with her rulin' the roost!

We all put by from our gardens this past summer. Our cow's still givin' plenty of milk for Tom and me to share. Buttermilk and cornbread still make for a tasty meal." "Even fair to middlin' meals is better than none at all. Reckin I could do mighty fine leavin' off a meal ever' day." Ollie patted her round stomach.

Eula loudly sniffed, then snorted. "I swan, Ollie, reckin it waren't hurt any of us. Certain fine, I still have my teeth and don't have to gum my vittles. Canned plenty from the garden too. Have plenty of kivers to stay warm and can still swing a hatchet and ax fer firewood," she murmured. "Hate to see so many families sufferin' now. Hurts my heart to see those scrawny babies with spindly laigs. Gotta start heppin' more."

Lois sat up straighter and tilted her head toward her aunt. "Wonder if the mill will be givin' out Christmas bags this year. I still look forward to the brown sack of candy, fruit, and small toys. I still play with my marbles. If the owners won't hep give out some Christmas cheer, we could do a family sack. It wouldn't be much, but a little's better than nothin'."

"We could git the twins , Lovey and Dovey, to hep too. Lovey talks up a storm, but she has a good heart. Both their husbands still have jobs, even if their pay is squat. None of us is rich, but we ain't poor neither.

"Them seven pecan trees in my yard full of pecans. Too many for even the squirrels to handle. Rather than storin' those pecans fer a rainy day or bakin' up pecan pies, I'll jist pass 'em on. Yep, and I'll put a jar o' my cucumber pickles in ev'ry poke too.

"All of us started work in the mills as youngins. It's hard to wake up in the mornin' as pooped as you was the night before. Being tuckered out weren't no excuse for missin' work. I was always afeared I was gonna fall off that little stool I stood on. But I was by Ma, and she took care o' me.

"We never had no choice on workin' or not workin'. It was what our family did. Papa and Ma worked at the mill, and so did we. It was expected. Everybody had to pitch in and hep to pay our own way. Hard work never hurt nobody, I always say.

"Don't ya' ever forgit that, Lois!" exclaimed Eula. She tapped her niece on the shoulder for emphasis.

"Now, what are you other two gonna add to the Christmas bag?" She peered around the porch.

Julie's spirited laugh interrupted her sisters' harangue.

When she was able to speak, three pairs of eyes suspiciously looked at her.

"Have ye lost yer ever lovin' mind, sis?" asked Eula.

"Oh, Eula, you shore can tell a person how to straighten up n' fly right!"

* * *

The sister of Julie and the aunt of Lois, Eula Petty never married again; she was a lifelong member of the Cowpens community. She was an active member of Cowpens Central Baptist Church until her death at age sixty-seven. Eula retired at age sixty from Clifton #1 Mill.

There was a closeness between Lois and Eula; Eula became a grandmother to Lois' sons after Julie died. During the summer, John would go spend a week with her, and then his brother Tom would do the same.

Everyone was welcome in her home; her front porch was the gathering place on Linda Street during the summer. The coal heater in her front room greeted those same neighbors when it was cold.

ANNIE MAE

The two-story boarding house proudly graced the corner of Green Street and Boyce Street in Union, South Carolina. It faced the Union Mill.

Painted white, like all of the other mill village houses, the windows sparkled in the June sun. Annie Mae Bobo was an excellent cook, but she also took pride in keeping her household spic-and-span.

Her eight male boarders felt blessed to pay room and board for one dollar a week. Two men shared each of the four upstairs rooms. The bachelors' ages extended from sixteen to nineteen.

Annie Mae and her daughter Noddie, a family nickname for Norma, washed the sheets and swept the rooms once a week. She provided her own handmade quilts for warmth in the winter. Opening the two windows in each room brought in fresh, and sometimes cool, air in the spring and summer. Available for spit baths and shaving were a pitcher, bowl, mirror, and towels.

A single light bulb in a brass socket, dangling from the ceiling, provided pale light at night. Two black wires loosely crawled up the walls and across to the socket from the switch beside the door. Green tape partially held the two wires together.

The outhouse was only yards from the back door. That forty-yard dash was not inconvenient to anyone, and two-holes were necessary for the house.

The usual daily breakfast stuck to the boarders' ribs through the long work day at the mill. Annie Mae cooked a fat cast-iron pot full of grits on her wood stove. Heaping spoonfuls of the grits filled half of each plate.

There were never any leftovers from the two long pans of piping-hot biscuits she served. Light as a feather, with their tops and bottoms browned to perfection, no one wanted to miss out on biscuits that tasted as good as cake. The queen of her kitchen timed their baking, so butter and honey melted and soaked into the bread immediately. Sopping up the overflow was not only allowed, but encouraged.

As the head of the household, Roy Lee Bobo, Annie Mae's husband, was always first in the line at the stove. Rubbing sleepy eyes, the other young men pushed and jostled for positions after him, but it was all in fun.

All knew every meal would fill them up. Serving plenty of what she had was one of the many rules that governed Annie Mae's life. She often reminded her children, as well as all within earshot, to "do right by the good Lord, hep yer own kin, hep others ye meet along the way."

During the workweek, she served breakfast at 6:00 a.m. sharp. Tardy boarders might not get all they wanted, but their portions were still ample. Annie Mae always put a bowl of grits and a biscuit by in the warmer of the stove for her two children, Noddie and Talmadge.

When her hens were laying well, she would fry eggs during the week, but usually this extra was for the weekend. Her hens and rooster were free-range, and it took time to search out their nests to find their eggs. Homemade grape jelly and apple butter were also offered as a treat.

Whiffs of percolating coffee often dragged the men out of bed. Most mornings, both of the ceramic pots were emptied. Coffee was the standard pick-me-up in this household.

Served in chipped and mismatched cups, coffee was continuously hot and ready to be drunk black or with some rich cream from the Bobo's two cows. Those two cows daily provided fresh milk and cream for the household. Annie Mae churned butter from the leftovers each day, as she listened to her favorite radio program, *The White Owl.*

The White Owl company sold cigars and sponsored a comedy show on the radio. A husband-and-wife team of Gracie Allen and George Burns were popular in their performances. Annie Mae laughed at all the silly comments made by the scatterbrained Gracie.

Lunch pokes for the boarders sat on the end of the table. On Monday, Wednesday, and Friday, two fried bologna sandwiches, wrapped in wax paper, were inside. Tuesday and Thursday were either sliced hard-boiled egg sandwiches, slathered with Duke's mayonnaise, or peanut butter and jelly sandwiches.

No one ever complained of the lack of variety in the food. In this June 1934, the United States was still in the throes of the Great Depression; all were thankful for their jobs, a clean place to sleep, and food in their bellies.

Elected last year, President Franklin Delano Roosevelt promised that the economy would improve. When the stock market crashed in 1929, paper money became scarce. Many banks and businesses closed for good. October 29 earned the name Black Thursday, as investors traded some sixteen million shares on the New York Stock Exchange in one day.

For the Bobos and other mill families, hard cash was never easily come by, but they had a large garden, chickens, hogs, and two cows that helped feed them year-round. Annie Mae canned any extra for the winter months that wasn't given away.

Bartering between neighbors and strangers was a way of life. Buying in bulk in the large barrels and bags at the company store also helped. Any leftover food scraps went to the hogs; cracked corn from the feed store was cheap for the chickens. Thriftiness had become penny-pinching, and recycling was compulsory.

All the boarders worked in the Union Mill, as did Roy, Annie Mae's husband, and they walked to work. Each man bought a Coke or Pepsi from the dope wagon to enjoy with his sandwiches. A caffeine jolt was often necessary to complete the afternoon's continuous, backbreaking work.

As they filed out of her house with pokes in hand to join the other mill workers walking to the mill, grins and words of thanks for their breakfasts were the norm. Though there was not much difference in their ages, Annie Mae mothered her boarders, and they recognized it. With little in worldly goods to their names and absent from their families, they valued their time at Annie Mae's.

Two rockers sat on her front porch. Carved on the newest one was her invisible name; no one sat there without permission. When she and Roy married in 1928, her father, Make, fashioned the oak chair for a wedding present. Its sentimental value far outweighed its monetary value to Annie Mae.

After the men noisily left for work, she headed for her rocker before the children woke. Knowing this sanctuary would soon be invaded by two rambunctious youngsters, she pulled out her can of Tuberose snuff, put a wad in her lip, and relished its first sting. Annie Mae always kept a tin handy in the pocket of her apron.

She gazed across the street to the mill pond. The spring branch kept it full, but even a small fire could deplete this water source. Each mill had a pond to counteract blazes of all sizes. All the plans for the mill villages included a pond, along with the company store, a school, and churches.

Looking down the dirt road, she glimpsed two men slowly walking. Sensing they would be her first visitors of the day, she continued to steadily rock. Annie Mae knew that all the biscuits were eaten for breakfast, except for the two in the warmer, and wondered if the strangers would stop.

As the men ambled closer, she noted the shuffling gait of one and the loose bandages falling from the other's arm. The shuffler needed a shave, and a film of dust and dirt covered his shirt and pants. Suspenders kept up the khakis that were too large for him. His traveling companion wore mended and torn overalls that were too short for his long legs. Large safety pins kept the galluses attached.

"Good morning, ma'am," said the red-haired shuffler. "Nice day, isn't it?"

He wore his newfound poverty like the heavy shield of one of King Arthur's knights. Annie Mae recognized a man of education and former means in his voice and manners.

The two tentatively stepped closer to her property line next to the road, but stopped before walking forward. These strangers paid attention to the invisible Private Property sign in front of her house. They also noted the small handwritten sign in front of the porch that said, "Welcome to Bobo's Boarding House."

"Howdy do, strangers. Hit's a mighty fine day. Are ye' headed fer town?" responded their prospective hostess. She spit over the rail, wiped her mouth with the hem of her patched apron, and sipped on her coffee.

"Yes'm, lookin' fer work. About any kind will do. I'se right handy with machines," answered the wounded man. "Saw that thar smoke from the mill's stack. Thought to talk to the super about a job or two."

Pushing back his blond hair as he took off his tattered straw hat, he continued, "Jist got off the CC&O, the Carolina, Clinchfield, and Ohio Railroad, that rolled in this mornin'."

Sheepishly, they both looked at their shoes, as if examining the torn soles and battered uppers.

The redhead spoke for both. "Ma'am, we jumped on the train from Tennessee. We didn't have any money to be paying passengers. In fact, we hid behind the big boxes in the baggage car to keep from being caught and thrown off. There were seven of us, all from different states. The others stayed at the hobo jungle back there, but we want to find work."

The men were anxious, and Annie Mae admired that they hankered after jobs.

Pressing her curly brown hair behind her ears, she stood up and walked barefoot to her front steps. It was summer, and shoes weren't necessary. Her blue-print dress was clean, but faded. As with her other two dresses, it hung barely below her knees. The buttons down the front matched and were sewn on to stay, and the belt buckle was her favorite shiny gray. Welcoming them, the meticulous seamstress brushed a speck of dirt off on the side of her dress.

Pointing to the bucket and tin cup hanging at her well, she instructed, "I'll git some towels fer ye' and put 'em on the steps. Thar's good tastin' water. Drink up and warsh up. Then ye' c'n meet me at the back."

Thankful grins appeared below their desperate eyes, and the two young and lanky men strode toward the well. Both thirst and hunger beleaguered their bodies. Simply because they could, they splashed each other like playing children. They intentionally soaked their bandanas before tying them back around their necks.

The front screen door slammed behind Annie Mae, as she headed down the hall toward the kitchen. Four doorways opened off the hall to the two bedrooms on the left and the kitchen and sitting room on the right. Stairs to the second floor stood on the left side. The two children split the space of the back bedroom; Roy and Annie Mae shared the front.

Annie Mae purposefully walked to the stove, opened the warmer door, and pulled out her children's breakfast plates. Heaping spoonsful of apple butter increased the small portions. The water heating in the pot on the stove for washing dishes was scalding, and she added it to the tepid liquid in her porcelain pan. After washing and drying two forks, she pulled the small plate of butter and a tin canister of milk out of the ice box. She sliced a generous portion of butter for the grits and another for the biscuits and poured two full glasses of milk for her guests.

Then she carefully measured out three tablespoons to make another pot of coffee.

Annie Mae used Luzianne coffee with chicory. She enjoyed smelling and drinking the rich, semisweet, caramel-like flavored blend. Many of the empty red and yellow cans now sat on shelves, filled with other objects. More visitors were likely on this unclouded and mild day, and she liked to have coffee on ready.

With the percolator back on the stove, she picked up the two plates and moseyed toward the back door and then the porch. Placing the two plates on the top step, she traveled the same way back to the kitchen for the glasses of milk. On her return to the porch, the two men stood quietly at the foot of the steps.

Annie Mae greeted them again. "Rec'n ye c'd do with some breakfast afore you do yer job-huntin' today."

She set the glasses down next to the plates and pointed to the food. From the hand of the shuffler, a small and worn portmanteau hit the ground with a thud; beside it landed an equally dog-eared cloth suitcase. A second invitation to breakfast was unnecessary.

Annie Mae wondered how long it had been since they had eaten; a hobo's life was grueling. Hobos had to jump on trains while they were moving. Riding the rails was dangerous. Lined up against starvation, begging became the daily standard option. Life in the hobo jungles was not always safe; the will to survive often took over any regard for civilized behavior.

"The super'll ask whar yer astayin' afore he'll say much. Tell 'm yer at Bobo's Boardin' House. Folks 'round here know I keep a r'spectable house," Annie Mae commented.

Over the past several years, Annie Mae had learned to not ask questions of her hobo visitors. But she listened when they wanted to talk. All their struggles were heartrending. The teenagers and younger men covered their struggles with bravado, but their eyes told the stories of old men.

For survival, hobos placed markings on fences, posts, and buildings for others to know where to find help or to steer them away from any trouble. The secretive hobo code helped this community of traveling workers remain safe, fed, and at work. There were railroad police that would lock them up for vagrancy and keep them from the possible standard wages of thirty-five cents for three weeks' work.

When Annie Mae learned of the hobo language, she asked a visitor one day to create signage for the Bobo house. He painted three images: one was a circle with a straight line over it, representing "Good people live here." The second was a lower case *r* that stood for "Care here if you are sick." "A kind-hearted lady" was symbolized by a dachshund missing his back legs. Annie Mae was thrilled with all of her advertisements.

Sometimes her memories of the hobos were hard to forget. Annie Mae had nightmares about the futures of many.

One day, a young, widowed mother with three dirty boys arrived at her back door. The towhead boys were five, seven, and nine, and all four had bed rolls tied to their backs. Their mother carried a small suitcase. This small family moved from one harvest camp to another, and all four picked whatever was being harvested.

Annie Mae sent them off with clean clothes and blankets, food, and full bellies. She had insisted on baths too. It was her pleasure to draw more and more buckets from the well to heat for their bathwater in the large tub placed in front of her stove. When Annie Mae took the boys to the porch to dry off and put on clean hand-me-downs, she heard the mother's painful, choking sobs when she was without her sons.

After this small family left, Annie Mae sat down and bawled for them. She continued to be astounded by those who were fighting to endure through these wretched and hopeless times. Often Annie Mae heard her mother's voice in her head saying, *Ye can't take it w' ye, hon. What ye got inside ye is what matters.*

Filling up her lip again with snuff, she gave the men permission to smoke after they ate. They pulled out several cigarette butts they had found on the ground and chose the two longest ones. Annie Mae washed and rebandaged the arm wound.

"Momma, who's 'at? Are they yer new friends?" Five-year-old Noddie peered out the screen door at the two men sitting on the steps. Seeing the empty plates on the porch, she continued, "I think I want my breakfast now too. Kin I have grits?"

With a start, Annie Mae turned to her sleepy-eyed child, who was standing in her wrinkled gown. Talmadge stood behind her; he showed his interest in the scene by putting his thumb in his mouth.

She rushed to think up another breakfast plan. The twenty-six-year old mother could not believe she had given her children's food away!

After scrambling eggs and preparing toast for her youngsters, Annie Mae took those few steps from her kitchen to the back door again. The two men were gone, but they left the plates and forks neatly stacked next to the glasses. Silently, she wished them well as she picked up the dishes.

Her thoughts went racing back to the first day Will Shipwash arrived at their house. It was a late afternoon in September. Four apple pies sat cooling in the two windows of her kitchen, and the two large iron frying pans of cornbread were in the stove warmer. The night meal was a beans and taters night; simplicity was on her mind after the craziness the previous night at City Park.

Everyone in town, it seemed, had enjoyed the annual City Park fair the night before. It was held at the city ball park at the foot of jail hill. This community gathering place derived its name from the jail beside the Court House at the top of the hill.

Originally the jail was a fort and powder magazine; the revamped structure was completed in 1823. This historical building was fashioned from granite and newly designed by South Carolinian Robert Mills, the architect of the Washington Monument. Along with offices, the cells were located on the first floor. Criminals were hung from the rafters in the large room of the second floor.

Yearly, the American Legion sponsored the fair. The children loved the carnival rides. There were baking, sewing, and canning contests for the women, and the Best in Show horses, goats, sheep, cows, and pigs received red-and-blue ribbons. Cows were the most popular choice to enter the contests, but last night a young boy exhibited some guinea pigs he had raised.

When Noddie and Talmadge saw those guinea pigs, they immediately clamored for their own. Miniature pigs or not, it didn't matter to Annie Mae. No pigs were going to live in her house; it was a short conversation.

All thoughts of the fair fled from Annie Mae's musings when she gazed out her kitchen window the next day and saw Will.

Shoving and pushing a wheelbarrow, filled with the unknown, was a middle-age man. He wore mismatched clothes and shoes without laces. Short and potbellied, he stumbled every few feet, but straightened himself and moved forward again. The wheelbarrow eased his awkwardness and improved his balance. He walked in a straight line across her yard, suddenly stopped, turned the wheelbarrow to the left, and headed for her back stairs.

He lurched to a stop, and his cowboy-style hat tumbled off his head. Awkwardly bending over, he captured the hat again. His hair was gray and sparse. He straightened and took a deep breath. Then he clumsily marched to her porch.

Annie Mae reached the door at the same time he did, and both nodded a greeting.

"Howdy do, ma'am. I be Will Shipwash. I want a job. I want a bed. Kin ye hep me?" Will spoke quickly and mumbled his words.

"Sit down, Mr. Shipwash, and I will fetch ye' a cup of water." Annie Mae wondered if this strange man was one of those angels unaware the Bible talked about Christians entertaining.

Several ladder-back chairs and benches were on the back porch, but Will was still standing straight in front of the door where she left him. Annie Mae pushed the door open and motioned him toward a chair. He looked at the chair and looked back at her. Then he repeated those looks.

"Mr. Shipwash, I'd be obliged if ye'd set in thet chair."

Will made a quarter turn and walked to the chair she pointed to. Annie Mae followed with the glass of water and handed it to him. Then she sat down in the bench in front of him. Silence reigned.

A few minutes later, Roy and the other boarders at the time walked to the porch from work. Roy stopped at the porch and sat down with his wife. He didn't understand the situation just by surveying the porch and wanted to be sure all was well.

Will stood, reached out his hand, and greeted Roy. "Howdy do, sir. I be Will Shipwash. I want a job. I want a bed. Kin ye hep me?"

Startled with the repetition, Annie Mae struggled to be still, though her mind was flooded with thoughts of how they could help Will. The two men conversed, but it was a slow process of quizzical looks and whispered mumblings on Will's side.

With skillful listening and patience, Roy discovered Will was from Spartanburg, South Carolina. Will's family had all died with the flu when the epidemic hit; Roy knew that was in 1918-1919. For sixteen years, Will had been walking from one place to another.

Shortly, the couple looked at each other, and Annie Mae nodded.

Roy said, "Will, I can speak to my super. He might have a job for ye in the mill. We allus need sweepers. Have ye been a sweeper afore?"

"I reckin so. Yeah, I think I can. I reckin I can sweep." He grinned and nodded at Roy.

Neither Annie Mae nor Roy could ever figure out exactly what was wrong with Will. His speech was simple, and the muttering was difficult to understand. It was the best he could do.

Roy helped Will get a job at Union Mill as a sweeper. He pushed two brooms up and down the aisles and worked the same shift Roy did. He brought his pay envelope home to Annie Mae on Fridays. She kept a little out for the household and kept the rest in a Luzianne coffee can in the sitting room. He would need the money one day. In the summer, he slept on a pallet on the porch. During cold weather, he had a pallet in the upstairs hall.

His quirks were endless, but ignored by the household and those at Union Mill. When the whistle blew, he knew it was time to go to work. Will had a routine to get himself out the door. Any variation or interruption flummoxed him.

Dust bunnies and dirt on any floor brought out a fanaticism in him, and he only settled down after he picked up or swept the unwanted soil. His mission was to clean floors, and he invited those who stood in his way to "move it." Those wayward ones who refused to comply in a timely manner with his orders found a broom shoving on their legs.

Not only did Roy and Annie Mae adopt Will Shipwash, but so did the mill families of Union Mill.

Chuckling at her reminisces of these past few months, a loud banging at the front screen interrupted her. A gravelly voice called her name; it was Uncle Cling.

Thomas Clingham Ingle, her father's older brother, had arrived for his yearly visit. Another place at the table would be set for only a week; Cling's stories would entertain everyone.

Cling owned Unaka Mountain outside Erwin, Tennessee, and he worked as a brakeman on the CC&O railroad. Every year, he rode free down to Union to visit with his family. Born on May 17, 1876, he was the second oldest child of William Gaither and Lizzie Ingle. When making a living from the land became impossible, some siblings stayed in Tennessee, while others moved to Upstate mill villages.

The Ingles in Tennessee, as well as those who lived in Ingle Holler, lived within rock-throwing distance of each other. Warm family ties were vital to Appalachian families, and they were close-knit.

Robert owned a shoe store in Johnson City, Tennessee. Clarence ran Ingle's grocery store, and Blaine owned Ingle's filling station in Erwin. Isaac was the town's handyman. The Ingles were not rich, but none lost their homes during the Depression.

Before Annie Mae could get to the front door, she saw Noddie and Talmadge scrambling up the steps on all fours. Both children grabbed a leg to welcome their visitor. Their great uncle immediately started frolicking with them.

Looking toward the roof, he hollered, "They got me! They got me! Lord, hep me, they got me!"

Trying to lift one leg and then the other, the fifty-eight-year old grumbled and protested as the children giggled and snorted. The shenanigans continued until the two attackers dropped to the front porch. Even though he was short, gangly, and stooped, Cling had more staying power.

Both adults continued to laugh at the children as they gasped for breath. Annie Mae tightly hugged her uncle, and he reciprocated.

"I'll take a taste of some of that good well water of yer'n, Annie Mae. Them children slapdab tuckered me out. What a welcomin' party! Jes ye look at 'em, rollin' around like puppies on yer porch."

Annie Mae shook her head at the sight, but decided getting rid of some energy was a good thing.

"Come set a spell, Uncle Cling. A bit ago, I drew a bucket. I baked a yaller cake this mornin' and whipped up white icin' with the egg whites. Ye can be the first to taste it. Right glad yer here!"

Noddie and Talmadge huffed and panted one last time. The oldest offered their services to taste cake too.

"Momma, we didn't have no grits this mornin'. Kin we have cake now?"

"Shore, that'll be a good idea, Noddie. Get Uncle Cling to tell you a story. I'll be back shortly," Annie Mae suggested.

"Unc'a Cling. Unc'a Cling. Tellus da' snake story. It makes me shake." Talmadge's little body shook, as he thought about it. But he still wanted to hear the terrifying tale again.

Cling picked Talmadge up and set him on his knee. Noddie leaned on the other knee, and the storyteller took command of the porch. Two pairs of eyes rounded and enlarged in anticipation.

"My third wife, Sally, straightened up our house ever mornin'. After she warshed dishes, she tooked to sweepin' and settin' the two rooms to right. One mornin' in June, she tarried a little long in the kitchen. Sally scurried into the bedroom, picked up dirty clothes, and made a pile of them close to the door. In a hurry to git to the cookin', she jerked off the one quilt on the bed. Then she retucked the sheet.

"Yankin' the pillers off' our bed, she screamed like a panther. Right der under the piller she had slept on was a coiled, diamond-back rattler.

Sally had woke it, and its rattles started singin'.

As it lunged at her, Sally threw the piller at it, high-tailed it to the door, and screamed agin. Now, a panther's scream is jest like a woman screamin'. I dropped my hoe and headed for the house lickety-split."

Both children glued their eyes to Cling's face.

"Then I heard the scream one more time. Sally ran out the door and jumped over the steps. She landed right at my feet in a muddle of petticoats and her dress and apron. 'Whar's the panther? Sally is it outside or inside? Whar is it?' Gaspin' for breath and gaspin' to speak, the skeered-to-death woman whispered, 'A snake in our'n bed, Cling. Thar's a rattler. It slept under my piller!'

"Her low voice grew louder with each word, and she finally bowed her head to the ground. 'Kill that rattlin' serpent, Cling. Bust its head in two! Now, Cling, now!' And so I did. Noddie and Talmadge, don't ye ever mess with no snake. Them rattles might sound purty, but they're a'tellin' you to hightail it away."

Both children were shivering now as they pictured in their minds the story of Aunt Sally sleeping with a snake.

Noddie, ever the older sister, patted Talmadge on the leg. "Don't ye worry none. I'll look under our pillers, Talmadge. I promise. Ain't no snakes are gonna sleep with us. Ever!"

Pounding the porch floor as hard as she could, the little girl stomped her foot for emphasis. Noddie had learned the importance of taking care of others from her mother.

Annie Mae brought out a tray with cake slices and glasses of cold water, and talk of snakes was forgotten.

Catching up with Tennessee family news and sharing South Carolina updates took over the afternoon on the porch. The children played marbles and jacks, before they went to the tire swing in the side yard. Their home rules included staying in the yard, unless permission was given to wander. With Cling visiting, they both kept checking in at the porch. Children never want to miss a good story.

After supper that night, the adults gathered on the porch to swap more tales. With lightning bugs winking all over the yard, Noddie, Talmadge, and the neighboring children ran wild in the yard after their blinking lights.

"Annie Mae, honey, there appears to be a tickle acomin' on in my throat," declared Cling. "I reckin a bit of my cough medicine would hep. Could ye git me some?"

His niece was a teetotaler, and she allowed no whiskey in her house. Cling brought his home brew with him, and she added her rock candy to it. Without speaking of the ingredients, the flavored liquid was now called cough medicine.

Though he had a steady job as a brakeman, he had his own still and regularly made white lightning out of his own corn crop. Some called it moonshine, because it was created at night under the light of the moon. All stills were well hidden in the mountain trees. This act was illegal; in the United States, anyone distilling spirits had to pay a federal tax. Of course, moonshiners paid no tax. The local police often ignored the home stills, because it wasn't hurting anyone. Cling had never been bothered by government revenuers either.

When Annie Mae returned from the kitchen, he grinned and said, "Thank ye kindly. Yer'a sweetheart to fetch it fer me. I will sleep like a baby tonight."

Nodding her agreement to his last statement, Annie Mae was silent. She loved her uncle, even if she didn't love his ways.

Roy joined them on the porch. Their greetings to each other were back slappings.

Annie Mae went back to her snapping of beans for tomorrow's big meal. Seasoned with fatback and cooked-in potatoes, these would be the first from this year's spring garden.

"Roy, don't believe I tols you 'bout rentin' the top of my mountain to the gov'ment last year. They cut their own road to the top and built a shortwave repeater up thar. Now, my little ham radio picks up people over the ocean."

"Thought about gittin' me one of them radios. Hit might be fun to listen to what's goin' on," replied Roy. "Tom Nance was talkin' about listenin' to some man at the South Pole. Believe his name was Admiral Byrd. Can hardly imagin' hit. Oliver made him one n' I reckin if he can do it, I can."

As they talked, Cling continued to sip. A couple of times, he started to nod off, but wouldn't give it up. "Nary a one of my five wives, God rest their souls, could fatten me up with their good cookin'. Hard to consider I've been a'widowed five times. All good wimmen, all good wimmen," Cling remarked out of the darkness.

"Uncle Cling, you are a good man when you're not drinkin' that cough syrup of yours."

* * *

Annie Mae was born in Unicoi County, Tennessee, in 1910. She was the oldest daughter of Make and Lizzie.

After Roy Bobo died of pneumonia at age thirty-eight, the widowed Annie Mae moved to Ingle Holler. She left her home and relocated into the basement of Fannie's house with Talmadge and Norma.

Her father, Make, took his meals with her; she was known in her family for her good cooking. Often she would cook an abundant Sunday meal, hoping some of the family would drop by. One or two usually did. Her coconut cakes and biscuits were most popular.

My husband, John, boarded with Annie Mae and her second husband, Johnny Thompson, for a year while he worked for the

Spartanburg County Block Map. She charged him six dollars for room and board.

JENNY BELLE

"Watch out, Kyle! You're not payin' attention to whar the front door is!" hollered Jenny Belle Yeary at her husband.

The short, chubby brown-haired wife was dressed in a faded blue print dress with a white collar. Sewn down the front were clear buttons. The dress's hem almost reached her ankles. As with all of her clothes, she had made the dress herself on her Singer sewing machine. The twenty-year-old foot treadle still worked well. Protecting the old dress, Jenny showed off her favorite apron with the yellow flowers trimmed in bright green rickrack. Rolled once into her scuffed and worn brown shoes were her usual short white socks. For stay-at-home clothing, she was gussied up.

Pulling a soft yellow handkerchief, edged in pale beige lace, out of her apron's pocket, she dabbed at her face. Jenny spent a lot of time with handwork in the winter, and tatting around handkerchiefs was a task she truly enjoyed.

Upstate South Carolina was sizzling in its usual heat wave in this summer of 1946. Sweating, not perspiring or glowing, was a daily consequence. Leaving the windows and doors open in their four-room house to the cooler night air and breezes was, at best, a temporary relief.

She jiggled seven-month-old Wayne on her hip. This was not his best time of day, and both mother and child knew it. Jenny pulled the well-worn pacifier out of her apron pocket, and the baby slurped it into his mouth. She brushed back his damp red hair from his flushed face and wondered again where his hair color came from.

"Virgil, that ain't a sack of potatoes you are holdin' onto. That's my piano," moaned Jenny. "Slow down! Dadgumit, the wheels are movin' too fast toward the front door."

Her husband, Kyle, kept moving the piano forward. "Jen, how many hundreds of times have we moved it to the porch for our Friday night prayer meetin'? I reckin Virgil and I know what we're doin'. Hold your taters now."

"Movin' this piano is as easy as falling off a greasy log backward, Jenny." Virgil shifted his end to the right. The muscles in his long arms steadied the black piano.

She still tapped her foot in frustration; the men were not being careful enough to suit her pickiness. Yes, her husband, Kyle Yeary, and next-door-neighbor Virgil Greene were always careful, but accidents still happened. If she weren't there to remind those two, there was no telling what might occur.

Reaching down, Jenny wiped her face, this time with a corner of her apron. When she was nine, she had a heat stroke, and the humid August heat was always hard on her. Her curly brown hair was damp and fell in ringlets around her face. Picking up one of her Holcombe Funeral Home fans, Jenny vigorously fanned herself and Wayne. She tended to collect the fans at funerals, and there was always one near at hand.

She had watched her modest home being built. With help from Jenny's Ingle kin, it was a simple task for easygoing Kyle. He liked to learn new things and read many educational magazines and books. Creating something from nothing was one of his gifts. As he often remarked, he liked to figure things out.

Little in their house on Excelsior Avenue in Union, South Carolina, had much of any monetary value, but the upright was a treasure. Jenny's piano had once been at home in Carnegie Hall in New York City; it was damaged in a fire. Jenny played by ear and pounded out tunes from the popular "St. Louis Blues" to the Southern gospel favorite "Mansion Over the Hilltop." Sometimes she played at their church, Green Street Methodist.

Kyle surprised her the first year they married with the scorched black piano. The gift of the piano was his finest hour. Kyle spent ten years of sweet talk and carrying a torch for her to convince Jenny to marry him. At age twenty-eight, when Kyle was thirty-eight, she finally said yes. The tall, skinny man from Kentucky never got over looking for ways to please her.

She cherished the gift and dusted the damaged Wurlitzer every day. Lace doilies protected its top surface, and a dresser scarf covered the bench. The singed marks gave it character, according to Jenny. Only Jenny Belle Yeary decided if a person was allowed to sit on that piano bench or not. Both kinfolks and friends had been surprised by being invited to find another seat in her parlor.

The two men easily lifted the piano over the lintel, through the screen door, and onto the porch.

Virgil walked down the steps to head home for supper. His black and gray hair was glued to his scalp from the exertion.

On his way to the road, he turned and chuckled as he spoke, "Jenny Belle, you are a sight for sore eyes when you get your feathers ruffled. I'm skedaddling now."

His toothy smile was a familiar sight, as he bowed with a flourish to Jenny.

With a loud "humph," Jenny turned her back and stomped back into the parlor.

"If I had my druthers, some neighbors might not act so big for their britches," muttered Jenny. "I'm as big for me as you are for you."

She spoke loud enough for Virgil to hear; the two jabbed each other on a regular basis.

The baby, Wayne, was used to a lot of moving and shaking when he was carried by his mother, and he began to doze off for a nap.

"Time's a wastin', Kyle. Family will be here before we know it. Let's cut that watermelon for a bite. You won't believe the tale I have to tell you."

Jenny's brother, Oliver Ingle, and her sister Annie Mae Bobo, and their aunt Fannie Ingle would be filling up the front yard and porch soon. Oliver and Lois would bring their two young boys and the new baby. The recently widowed Annie Mae and her two children would walk with Aunt Fannie. When Annie Mae's husband Roy died of pneumonia, she lost their boarding house and had nowhere to live. Fannie offered the small family of three the bottom floor of her house.

Just like their Ingle parents had farmed and worked the pulpwood business together with their siblings in Erwin, Tennessee, now their children and spouses worked in the various mills in Union. Mill jobs paid a salary every week; cash money wasn't always available on a farm. The seven Ingle men and their three sisters escaped the hard scrabble life in Tennessee because of the move to South Carolina.

Kyle and Jenny sat down at the hexagonal kitchen table; five-year-old Bruce was at his place, playing with his blue-and-red spinning top. The boy liked the squeak of the metal as it turned. Bruce leaned back in his ladder back chair to watch the top from a different angle. Out of the blue, both boy and chair toppled, and Bruce screeched in fright.

"Son, you know better than to lean back in that straight chair!" exclaimed Kyle. "I've told you afore. Next time I catch you at it, I'm gonna tan your hide."

Bruce nodded in quick jerks. His straight hair kept falling over his face. He was familiar with what a tanning was like.

Jenny squinted at her son to see if there was any blood to be washed or bandaged. She needed to wear her glasses all the time, but she disliked their addition to her face. Often her vanity won over seeing.

Kyle picked up his son first and then righted the chair. Sniffling a little, the boy reached immediately for the top and was side-tracked back to the entertainment of the whiny top. The oilcloth tablecloth was his favorite play surface in the house. The tan background outlined his roads, and the colorful flowers were mountains to go around. With his wooden horses carved by Kyle, the youngster journeyed on new adventures every day.

Bruce pretended he was the Lone Ranger; that was his favorite radio program. The Lone Ranger didn't have a Christian name, and he wore a black mask. His friend was an Indian named Tonto, and the two caught robbers and criminals of all kinds. Every so often, Bruce would shout, "Hi-yo, Silver! Away!" just like the Lone Ranger would call out to his horse before they took off on a rescue mission.

The boy had natural rhythm, and he would bounce his horse along to the rhythm of the theme music. The final part of the *William Tell Overture* sounded just like galloping horses or a hero who was racing to the rescue. Bruce would often stand taller as he pretended to be the hero himself.

Jenny Belle gave a sigh of relief that injury wasn't the result of this small disobedience. She put a slice of watermelon on a plate, pushed it toward Bruce, and moved the favorite top out of the way. The sleeping baby shifted with his mother's movements; it was like a game of follow-the-leader, only between the two of them.

"Kyle, you won't believe what that young'un Joe Fox did today. I do feel right sorry for the handsome boy with his wife leavin' him, but he's not thinkin' straight. He's as lost as last year's Easter egg.

I was sweepin' the front porch for tonight, looked across the yard, n' saw that pore young'un alayin' in the middle of the road. So I walked out there to him and told him to git up. There he lay in his worn-out and dirty overalls. His mussed hair needed a good brushing. Joe looked at me with those sad, beagle eyes and said, 'Miz Yeary, I can't take it no more. I'm gonna lay right here 'til some car comes n' runs over me.' Then, dadjimit, he up and shut his eyes. He was like a dead pig in the sunshine."

Rolling his eyes, Kyle took another bite of watermelon.

Jenny Belle continued, "I have never seen a grown man give up like that, Kyle. Since she left him, he hasn't hit a lick at a snake. I felt obliged to help him out. So I hiked back to the house, loaded my pistol, and marched out to him again. I was holdin' out my Smith and

Wesson, n' I told him plain. 'Take my pistol, and do it yourself. Don't get someone else involved in your own misery.'"

Kyle listened silently to this latest escapade, but then choked as he swallowed. The tall, wiry man, who was slowly balding, worried about his wife's tendency to ignore possible consequences of her actions. Jenny's quickness to take matters into her own hands constantly surprised him. Rather than listening to reason or common sense, Jenny always responded with her heart.

"Joe Fox looked at me like I was some crazy woman. He put his hand up and pushed my gun clean away. I stood there lookin' down at him with him starin' back at me for a few minutes. Then I gave him one last hard stare, turned around, and left him in the road. I didn't glance back until I was back on our porch. Then I saw he was shufflin' back to his home with his head hung low.

"Kyle, have you ever heard tell of such?" While she shook her head in disbelief, Jenny Belle took a big bite of her watermelon.

"Well, shut my mouth, Jen," Kyle slowly responded. "You've got more nerve than Carter's got liver pills and ain't afeared of nuthin' 'cept thunderstorms."

Jenny Belle nodded her head in agreement and handed the sleeping baby over to him.

Then she reached to the center of the table to push a hydrangea back into the bowl. Jenny Belle was pleased with the large blossoms on her bushes this year. The bushes were on the corner of both sides of the front porch, and the sweet and spicy scent hovered around the entrance to the home.

Contrasting with the oranges, browns, and yellows of the bowl, the blue flowers brought Mother Nature inside. Autumn Leaf was the name of the tableware pattern, and it was the specialty piece for the spring collection made by Hall China Company. Jenny was delighted to own it.

Every Tuesday, Virgil Greene made his rounds to sell coffee, tea, spices, grocery, and household items. His delivery wagon was a dark, Nash station wagon full of offerings from the Jewel Tea Company. To thank their customers, the company offered specials to their patrons. One of the most popular was the Autumn Leaf china; its elegance was in the gold rim adorning each piece.

Jenny Belle, as many of her neighbors, depended on Virgil's weekly visits to refill their larder. Even if they had owned a car, neither she nor Kyle could drive.

Jenny longed for elegance and a gracious life. Having pretty bits and pieces in her home brought a contented smile to her face. Item by item, she was hoping to own a whole dinnerware set of Autumn Leaf one day. She smoothed an imaginary piece of dust off the bowl and flicked it on the floor.

Their energetic child interrupted the meal once again.

"Papa, I'm the Lone Ranger!" Bruce suddenly declared. "There's a man trapped in the coal mine like you were, n' he can't get out. My horse Silver'l get me there in time."

Both parents watched their son as he raced the wooden horse all over the table.

Kyle stared at Bruce in amazement. He was sure that his young son had not heard that story. In the spring, Kyle's older brother Lige visited for a few days. The brothers had reminisced about growing up in Middlesboro, Kentucky. Much of the time, Bruce played at their feet. Obviously he had been listening at the same time.

The memory of that terrifying day could still wake Kyle up at night drenched in sweat.

Four families worked the small mine on their property in Middlesboro. The outcropping wasn't big enough for the mining companies to be interested in, but it provided a living for the families. The four went in together to buy an old dump truck and sold the coal to the power company.

The ear-splinting crackling of the earth and rocks roared in Kyle's ears before it buried him. He couldn't move because of the weight. His headlight broke, and the darkness was threatening and grim. There were no shadows. Surrounded on all sides by the rubble, the confining space felt instantly claustrophobic.

Gasping for air, he heard his brothers, Lige and Walter, hollering his name. Then there was the sound of picks and shovels moving the debris. Within minutes, Kyle saw the pinpoint of Walter's headlight. His eyes squinted and focused on that dot until he saw his brother's face, smeared with coal dust, under it. The bruising to his body was severe, but mercifully he had no broken bones.

Twenty-year-old Kyle never worked in the family coal mine again. He hoboed on the CC&O freight train to South Carolina and never left.

Seeing Kyle scowl, Jenny reached over to pat her husband's clenched fist. She knew he had fallen back into a day he didn't want to remember. Soon he relaxed and nodded at her in thanks. Then she stood, carefully picked up his plate and hers, and walked to the porcelain sink.

Originally, the green sink was a light fixture in the Union Mill; it hung from the ceiling. Oliver, Jenny's brother, and Kyle cut a hole in the counter, turned the fixture upside down, and ran a drain pipe from the bottom of it to the outside. Their house then boasted indoor plumbing.

Bruce had filled the water bucket from the outside well, and the porcelain pan was now all set for the rinse water. Hot water was already in her iron kettle. In this hot weather, Jenny hated to heat the house, but clean dishes were important to her.

Jenny's mother used to say "cleanliness is next to godliness," and her three daughters kept clean houses. Washing with the washboard in the large tub outside was not an easy task, but watching the clothes swing and float on the outside line was magical. The sheets billowed and puffed like clouds. Overalls, shirts, aprons, and dresses danced on their own stages.

Jenny watched the hazy antics through her window and then turned back to her husband.

"Kyle, the back screen door is gittin' plumb full of cotton balls to keep the flies out. I don't rightly like how it looks. The black-and-white reminds me of a polka dot pattern gone all catawampus and out-of-sorts. It plain irritates my eyes. How about puttin' a new screen in this weekend? I reckin you could trade Oliver for some screen wire. He said last week there was some left from his rescreenin' their windows. He'd be pleased to get a couple of jars of my blackberry preserves and some quarts of our canned green beans. He was the onliest one of us who didn't complain when Momma sent us blackberry pickin'. Lois has her hands-full with workin' those long hours in the mill, tending those two young'uns, and now a new baby. I want to help 'em out some."

"I have to fill my sassafras orders this weekend, Jen. They're a pilin' up. An' you know I don't like to be beholden to nobody, and them families are acountin' on me," responded Kyle. "I had a mind to put us in a new screen too. It'd jist have to be this weekend."

With her hands on her hips and smiling now, Jenny said, "I do declare, Kyle. That piddlin' mail-order business keeps you busy."

One Sunday last year, the Ingle clan was sitting around after churning homemade ice cream. Since it was peach season, all had fresh peaches in their yards. They only had to buy a chunk of ice from the ice truck and sugar from the company store. Fresh milk was available because each family owned one cow. Everyone, including the children, was content and chock-full of the frozen dessert after scraping the churn over and over.

The men talked of ways to earn more money; it was challenging each month to extend their monthly salary of thirty-five dollars. Extra was not in their sparse checks.

Jenny and the rest of the women made their husbands' shirts out of pig feed and flour sacks, but overalls had to be purchased for work in the mills. The men wore out their one pair of high tops until they couldn't be repaired at home anymore with their cobblers' hammers.

Each summer, they cut off the boys' overalls and let out hems for the girls. The children, as well as the women, mostly went barefoot in the summer to save their shoes.

Food from their gardens, eggs and meat from the chickens, milk from that one cow, and meat from their hogs supplemented their diet of beans and taters or taters and beans. Canning stretched the garden offerings into winter. As their gardens came in, the women helped each other put up their vegetables. They even cooked preserves out of watermelon rinds.

Kyle had the inspiration to sell sassafras root for tea; there were plenty of trees in the nearby woods. Even young Bruce could help him pull up the tubers and wash them. After the roots were cleaned with steel wool and cut up, he cut the roots in cubes and sold it by the square inch.

He chose to wrap the packages in brown paper and string, and the postage was only a nickel. He soon had repeat customers. Kyle was creative and made his own printing plate and only had to run an advertisement every two months. His side business proved his notion that people will buy anything if it is advertised.

The tea was flavorful; it did not need the addition of lemon or sugar. Scores used it to treat high blood pressure or the effects of a cold and flu. Others consumed it for gastrointestinal problems. One square inch would make sixty-four cups of tea. It was a bargain remedy that contributed to people feeling young again.

Jenny handed Kyle a cup of his favorite Eight O'Clock Coffee. He savored that one added cup in the evening. Whenever he ran out, he walked to the A&P, The Great Atlantic and Pacific Tea Company, grocery store on Main Street. They sold the coffee beans and provided the grinder. The good-hearted man was serious about his coffee, and the other Ingle men had joined him in liking this brand.

Even though she didn't drink much coffee, Jenny loved the smell of the coffee brewing on the stove. Her eight-cup tin percolator took two scoops to make the perfect cup. Bruce enjoyed watching the coffee bubble up in the small glass piece on the lid.

Jenny took a last swallow of tea left in her cup. She picked it up and carefully crooked her little finger before she finished it.

In one of the *Woman's Day* magazines Kyle had bought her at the A&P, she saw a picture of a group of women having a tea party. All of them had on hats and gloves, and their pinkies were bent. From that day on, Jenny made sure to follow their example when she drank her tea.

Astounding social habits could be learned from that little two-cent magazine, and Jenny scrutinized each copy until it was threadbare. She dreamed and cherished thoughts of living in a more cultured society, but knew it was beyond possibility. Even to a woman with only a fifth grade education like Jenny, being presentable was important, though she couldn't rise above her raising.

Kyle had borrowed a well-worn copy of her magazine to start a fire one day; her response was a hissy fit that had not been forgotten by either of them.

After putting a pinch of her Checkerberry snuff in her lower lip, Jenny wiped off the table and straightened a stem in her bowl of flowers. Then she went over the few pieces of furniture in her parlor. Most of the room received a lick and a promise, but dusting her well-worn Bible was a tender task. She straightened doilies and doodads and turned her copy of her favorite book, *Little Women,* to a more pleasing angle on the radio console.

The March women also lived in poor circumstances, but Marmee taught her daughters the importance of helping others who had less, even when they had little to share. Jenny believed that dealing with poverty was hard, but not lending a hand was unthinkable. As she went about tidying the tidy, she hummed and then sang one of her favorite hymns, "In the Sweet By and By."

There's a land that is fairer than day,
And by faith we can see it afar;

For the Father waits over the way
To prepare us a dwelling place there.

In the sweet by and by,
We shall meet on that beautiful shore;
In the sweet by and by,
We shall meet on that beautiful shore.

We shall sing on that beautiful shore
The melodious songs of the blessed;
And our spirits shall sorrow no more,
Not a sigh for the blessing of rest.

To our bountiful Father above,
We will offer our tribute of praise
For the glorious gift of His love
And the blessings that hallow our days.

Jenny's forlorn hope for an easier day was put aside for now. As had always been necessary, she would make do.

* * *

Kyle Yeary courted Jenny Belle Ingle for ten years; he was patient and finally won her over. Kyle was ten years older than his bride.

Born in 1911, the year after her sister Annie Mae, Jenny Belle had an amusing sense of humor, enjoyed life, and loved people. Good manners were important to her. For family and friends that dropped by unexpectedly, she would have a little surprise to give, even if it was only a spoonful of grits leftover from breakfast.

Her sons say that she always listened to them and encouraged them to do their best.

LOIS

"Oliver," Lois called to her husband from the kitchen.

"Ol'!" A more insistent tone entered her voice.

"Ol'!" Her voice was higher-pitched this third time; she needed him to wake up now.

Oliver Ingle's feet finally hit the floor next to their bed. Even though he had never before heard her scream in ten years of marriage, he recognized her cry for help.

In four long strides, he reached the open door to the kitchen. Slithering across his wife's feet was a two-and-a-half-foot copperhead. Her blue eyes met his blue eyes, and he nodded reassurance. A faint smile answered; she trusted Oliver.

The snake carried on its quest for a random mouse, so it didn't linger on Lois' foot. Ignoring the breakfast crumbs that needed sweeping, it held its distinctive yellow tail off the floor and slid on.

Standing quietly in the doorway, Oliver stretched his right arm up to retrieve his rifle. The rifle hung on a rack above the door. Before he stepped to the chest to pick up some bullets, he quietly asked, "Where are the young'uns?"

With a slight signal of her head, Lois indicated the yard. She stood unmoving in front of her wood stove. Her shaking hands rested on the biscuit sandwiches she was making for Oliver's breakfast.

The snake continued its leisurely glide across the floor toward the kitchen table. Its forked tongue investigated the Ingle kitchen.

Deliberately, Oliver loaded the 22 Remington rifle, took aim, and fired several rounds. He missed the snake, but left permanent holes in the floor. Easing toward the light-brown serpent with its classic hourglass markings, he noted the two-inch fangs full of poison.

The tail of the intruder quivered in agitation; the bullets startled it. There was no safety under the table.

The hunter had a plan. With the rifle still cocked, he maneuvered to the front of the snake and lowered the barrel. After putting its curious tongue in front of the barrel, it lost its copper head.

Two tow-headed boys watched the spectacle through the shut screen door; they had run from the yard at the first sound of gunfire.

"Wow! Good shot, Papa!" shouted John.

Nodding his head in agreement, Tom, the eight-year-old, opened the door. "That was one stupid snake!"

Oliver carried the wiggling dead snake out the door on a broom handle.

John excitedly asked, "Papa, whar' you gonna put it? It's a long 'un. I reckin it's close to ten feet!"

Although it was much shorter, it looked massive to the four-year-old.

"Will you bury it?" questioned Tom. "Kin I take it to show the cousins, 'specially Talmadge? This'uns fatter than the one we saw near the woodpile last week."

Oliver kept walking toward the clothes line, then draped the snake's body over the rope.

A man of few words, he turned to his sons. "S'pect a hungry owl or hawk will enjoy a tasty meal from this'un. There are natural laws that take care of all God's creatures. I sorta' enjoy watchin' His order of things. If you boys can sit quiet on the back steps, you might jus' see this free dinner disappear. I'm gonna see about your ma." Taking two steps at a time up the steep steps to the back porch, he called out to Lois, "Hon, you doing all right?"

She sat at the kitchen table holding her pregnant belly with both hands. Her long brown hair hung in waves over her face. Pushing back the ringlets, she turned toward her husband. "My lan', I didn't smell it, Ol. I always smell a snake when it gits close to me. I've been sittin' here wondering what happened."

She stopped talking to spit in the nearby can. Since she dipped Chinaberry snuff, a nearby can was a necessity. "All I kin figure is my nose was plumb full of that fryin' sausage fur your breakfast. That snake was shore a surprise!"

Lois could smell a nearby snake, and the family believed her. She proved it to Oliver one day when they were walking back on the path from Jenny's. Her warning about smelling one was quickly reiterated by a jab in the ribs only a few seconds before he stepped on a black snake lying across the path. He never questioned her again.

On the way to pour a cup of coffee, he tenderly patted her shoulder and then knelt to give her a hug. "Why don't you take it easy this mornin'? Aren't you n' the women folk quiltin' this afternoon? The boys and I can fend for ourselves. I'll keep 'em busy outside."

"I swept up the mess from that snake and sent those sorry remains out the door, but there's a bit more readying up to do. I'd appreciate yore mindin' 'em a while. I need to dust the living room and straighten up a bit."

Lois smiled at her husband for his thoughtfulness and rose to put his biscuits on a plate. She laid the iron frying pan back on a burner and broke three eggs into the grease, where she had cooked the sausage patties. Oliver liked his eggs medium, and Lois watched them carefully to be sure they didn't overcook. Cooking on a wood stove could be tricky, because the iron tended to get hotter the longer it was on a burner. Within minutes, she hand-delivered the breakfast plate to Oliver.

Lois and Oliver used white plates, but she had bought six tin plates covered in gray porcelain with black decorative spots for her sons and their cousins. The dishes were ugly, but Lois believed that children weren't careful with what they handled. Tin plates bounced when they hit the floor.

All the chickens in Ingle Holler were free-range. Oliver built a coop for hers to nest and lay their eggs. Lois kept and fed eight to ten cluckers, along with one rooster. When she had a hankering for fried chicken, they had no fear of her getting close. Lois easily grabbed one and then wrung its neck.

Most of the hens laid one egg a day. Sometimes a hen would hide her egg to set on it in the fall or winter. Lois was a master at finding those secretive eggs. Baby chicks would die in the South Carolina cold days, but spring and summer chicks were welcome.

The fifty-pound chicken feed sacks and hog feed sacks were constructed out of sturdy cotton material. An empty bag was quickly recycled into dish rags, as well as shirts and underwear for the boys. Recycling was a way of life, not a choice.

Union Mill, SC

Ingle Holler was in Union, South Carolina. Make Ingle, the patriarch, bought thirty acres of land on the outskirts of the city from Excelsior Mill. Then he offered the opportunity to his ten adult children to buy a plot from him at a good price. Oliver bought two acres, and five of his brothers purchased lots also. Make's daughter Jenny and her husband chose five acres, and then Make gave his widowed daughter, Annie Mae, five acres.

The Ingle clan worked hard. Vegetable gardens flourished in the rich soil. Each family owned several peach trees and raised chickens and hogs. For the winter, the women filled Mason jars with vegetables and fruit.

The property was convenient. Access to their work in the cotton mills of Union or Excelsior was an easy two-mile walk on the foot path. There was no road into the hollow, except some ruts down the hill for a wagon.

Outhouses were behind every home.

Necessities came from the land, and the families were self-sufficient. Engineered by Make, a man-made spring furnished water. From the Ingle Branch flowed about two thousand gallons of water a day. They used the pine and cedar trees on the land to build and heat their houses. What one needed, another shared.

Make was a widower and a retired night watchman from Union Mill. All his life, he carefully saved from his paycheck, and the money multiplied. Growing up in Buncombe County, North Carolina, his father's family had lived close together. His fondest memories of childhood were exploring the woods and mountains with his cousins; he wanted the same for his grandchildren. They called him Grandpa, and his response was a quick grin. He spent most days going from one household to another lending a hand to whoever needed help.

Every inch of land in the hollow was an outdoor playground to be explored and enjoyed by all the Ingle cousins. Swimming and catching minnows and crawdads with their hands filled the days of the children during the summer. Climbing trees and playing roll-the-bat, cowboys and Indians, or hide-and-seek were other pastimes. When it rained, they played under the houses.

Even though it was late April of 1945 and America was fighting in World War II, there was a sense of the ordinary during most days and nights in Ingle Holler.

As Oliver ate and then leisurely smoked his first cigarette of the day, Lois poured him another cup of coffee. He liked the Prince Albert tobacco that he bought at the company store. Packaged in a red tin with gold lettering, he kept it handy in the bib pocket of his overalls, along with a pencil and his pocket watch.

While he sat at the table, Lois started washing dishes and straightening up the kitchen. She owned two white porcelain bowls with red rims: one was for washing and the other for rinsing. She heated the water that the boys brought in buckets from the spring on the stove. Periodically, she checked on her sons outside.

Continuing to tidy up the kitchen, Lois declared, "Ol, we've been seein' a lot of those copperheads. Think I'll git Tom and John to stick some matches in the ax holes on the choppin' block. I reckin I can still light them off with the rifle. I jest need more practice to be a better sharpshooter. Don't like it one bit that those varmints are a'comin' in my kitchen." She glanced out the screen. "Lan sakes alive! Them two whippersnappers of our'n are still a'sittin' on the steps. You must have bribed them with something real good."

Oliver chuckled. "They are waitin' on some hawk to come to dinner."

"I was thinking this mornin' about when my momma died. Can't rightly believe it was six years ago. It has jist been too long. For no reason, I woke up that night. Standin' at the foot of the bed was Momma, and she waved at me. Quick as lightnin', she disappeared. I was plumb shore as certain it was a dream at three in the mornin'. Warn't too long 'fore Sheriff Rochelle Boyle showed up to tell me she had died at the mill."

She paused and snatched her apron up to wipe her eyes. "That was a sad time. I miss my momma. Times I wish we had a phone. Other times, I don't. Bad news travels fast ennyways."

Lois was four months pregnant, and her usual cotton dress was getting tight across her stomach. With no success, she tried to loosen the dress and decided it was time to make a couple of larger ones. She loved to sew and do other handwork. Creating a useful item out of scraps was pure pleasure, and she was proud of her sewing machine.

Tom and John's high-pitched voices reached her from the yard.

Oh, we don't want her, you can have her,

She's too fat for me,

She's too fat for me . . .

Lois exclaimed, "What the Sam Hill are they up to now?"

And then the boys started their serenade once more, adding the throwing of arms and jumping up and down. It was a show for their momma, and she responded with laughter and clapping at their antics. Their singing and her mirth continued until she laughed so hard she cried. Thinking that his family had all lost their minds, Oliver joined his wife at the window.

This couple tended to fret little about the ups and downs of life. The highs were always celebrated, and they chose to struggle through the harder bumps. As with most days, this Saturday had taken a better turn since the copperhead visit.

Oliver shook his head, grabbed his Stetson hat, and headed toward his older brother Richard's house. His hand tools were waiting for him there. More kitchen cabinets were needed for the kitchen. Harvey was the third son, and Oliver and he were gifted at woodwork. Richard's wife, Gracie, would feed them lunch for their goodwill. Since she was a fine cook, the trade-off worked well for all.

"Come on, boys," Oliver yelled. "I'm a'needin' your help."

Saturday morning shenanigans halted. Jostling each other and playing tag as they went, Tom and John followed their father.

Still chuckling from the singing, Lois took her broom and dust cloths to the living room. Placing the cleaning supplies on the floor, she lowered the quilt frame from its hooks in the ceiling. When not in use, Oliver had created pulleys and ropes to store the frame out of the way. By lowering it now, the women could go right to work. She walked around, straightening the cloth pieces not sewn in place.

Her two favorite pictures caught her eyes. A boy and a girl were holding hands, crossing a rickety bridge in one. There was a guardian angel hovering over them and the angry water below. In the second picture was a single young blonde girl clinging to a large stone cross with ocean waves washing up around her feet.

At the bottom of the second one were the words, "Dedicated to Iris Emory." Iris was Lois' younger sister who died at three months with whooping cough. Growing up as an only child, Lois often wished for a sister. Even now, there were times she felt that void. She dusted the frames and glass of that picture first.

Lois tended to sing while working in her house or in the garden. As she cleaned today, she sang her favorite song, "When They Ring Those Golden Bells."

There's a land beyond the river,
That we call the sweet forever,
And we only reach that shore by faith's decree;
One by one we'll gain the portals,
There to dwell with the immortals,
When they ring the golden bells for you and me.

Don't you hear the bells now ringing?
Don't you hear the angels singing?
'Tis the glory hallelujah Jubilee.
In that far-off sweet forever,
Just beyond the shining river,
When they ring the golden bells for you and me.

We shall know no sin or sorrow,
In that haven of tomorrow,

When our barque shall sail beyond the silver sea;
We shall only know the blessing
Of our Father's sweet caressing,
When they ring the golden bells for you and me.

When our days shall know their number,
And in death we sweetly slumber,
When the King commands the spirit to be free;
Nevermore with anguish laden,
We shall reach that lovely Eden,
When they ring the golden bells for you and me.

Walking around the quilting frame, Lois went to the brick fireplace, which was the house's main source of heat. During a cold Southern night, she would sometimes warm a brick on the hearth and put it at the foot of their beds for added warmth. There were several of her quilts on each bed. She swept the ashes from under the grate and added them to the ash bucket. Leaving the coal bucket where it was, she then swept the hearth. Even with all the daily dirt being tracked in the house, Lois was a meticulous housekeeper. With female kin visiting for the afternoon, an extra wipe was in order.

Her sewing machine was a Singer treadle model with a scarf covering it. Always ready to light when she needed extra brightness was a kerosene oil lamp, placed in the middle of the machine case. The dark green sofa, a stuffed brown chair, and an extra straight chair completed the seating in the cozy room.

Sweeping herself out the door, she bent over to look under all the furniture for any escaped dust bunnies. Then she realized the three windows were cloudy.

Because of the closeness of Camp Croft and their war maneuvers, there was a cross of tape on each pane of all the windows of the house. So far, the windows had rattled, but none had broken. Lois went back to the living room windows and cleaned them until they sparkled. She didn't want any of the women to strain their eyes on the minute stitches required for quilting that afternoon.

The bead board walls were painted light blue to reflect light during the day, and this also brightened the room. Lois was partial to sunlight. Perhaps this was a result in the long years working in various mills.

"Momma, we're starvin'!" exclaimed Tom as the two boys rushed into the kitchen, the screen door slamming behind them.

John added, "A hawk flew over, jest like an airplane, and snatched that snake. You should have seen it, Momma. The hawk never even stopped. Then it flew over the trees two times! Reckin that hawk was right proud."

"Warsh your hands, now, and I'll see to your emptiness." Lois had cooked pinto beans with salt pork the day before, and there was enough for all three to have a plate with the leftover cornbread. She spooned out three platefuls. "Use that Octagon soap, John. I'm watchin' you. Tom, that towel is for dryin', not for slappin' your brother on the leg."

There was a wash basin on a small table next to the back door. As usual, water ended up on the floor and on the boys. Lois wondered how life would be if this new baby was a boy. There was nothing wrong with her sons' get up and go; they were always moving.

"Settle down, you two. You're like worms in hot ashes. Bow your heads now, and let's say the blessin'. Lord Jesus, thank you for this food. Thank you for this family. And thank you for takin' such good care of us. In your name I pray, amen."

"Momma, whar's the mayonnaise?" Tom asked. "I want to put some on my beans.""Me too," echoed John.

As she stood up to get the mayonnaise out of the icebox, Lois turned to John.

"John William, if yer brother was to jump off a cliff, would you jump after him?"

"Sure would, Momma. I could hep him!" responded her youngest with an ear-to-ear smile.

The boys slathered their beans with the mayonnaise and then mixed it all up. Lois tried not to look, as she put some pickles on her own plate.

Finishing quickly, the boys went back out the door to join Oliver again. Their plates were clean. As was their usual end to a meal, a burping contest started before they were completely out of their mother's hearing. Neither of them needed any additional practice.

"My word, I don't know how they make such noises," Lois said to the dishes.

As she covered the drying dishes with a cloth, she heard Joanna's "howdy," as she climbed the back stairs. She mimicked Minnie Pearl in her greetings.

Harvey Ingle's wife, Joanna, was the mother of four girls, Grace, Doll, Mary Ann, and Betty. She and Lois had grown closer since John's birth, because Joanna had delivered him. The home delivery wasn't planned.

Oliver had to walk one mile to get to the doctor's house, and the baby didn't wait. By the time Oliver and Dr. Guess arrived, Joanna had wrapped John in a blanket and laid him on the bedside table. The doctor pronounced mother and son as fit as fiddles and complimented Joanna on her midwifery skills.

Jenny Belle, Oliver's sister, and Fannie, Oliver's aunt, arrived shortly. Jenny Belle was talking without taking a breath, as usual, and the reticent Fannie rolled her eyes at her companion.

Joanna, Jenny Belle, and Fannie dragged three kitchen chairs to the living room. Lois pulled up the straight chair, and the four commenced their afternoon of sharing gossip, news, dipping snuff, and quilting. Their fingers deftly crafted small stitches in the cloth.

Within minutes, they heard the soldiers at Camp Croft practicing at some of the 250 target ranges located on 167 acres. Land once used for the farming of tobacco and cotton barely a mile away became a mock war zone. During certain hours, the artillery sounds were like continuous thunder.

This US army military camp was a training camp for the infantry. These repeated exercises included the use of pistols, rifles, mortars, machine guns, and howitzers. A cacophony of battle sounds drowned the country side and Union county, as the army schooled the loss replacements and fillers for war. Every eighteen weeks, a new group of selectees received instructions and practice to make them soldiers skilled in weaponry.

South Carolina Senator James F. Byrnes and other leaders from Spartanburg and Union counties had lobbied hard for this Replacement Training Camp to be built in the Upstate. The economy of both counties boomed from the beginning, particularly the cotton mills. The armed forces needed cloth for uniforms, tents, and, and blankets.

"Still can't rightly believe how the good Lord kept Oliver out of this war, Lois," said Jenny Belle. "He was ready, willin', and able until that freak accident on his way to Fort Jackson."

"I didn't cry when he left," Lois said, "but tears flooded my cheeks the rest of the day. I holed up in this very room." She looked at her friends as she looked back in her memories.

"I was pert shore I wouldn't be seeing him ag'in. Those thoughts took both my breath and senses away. I couldn't seem to hit a lick at a snake. Held John almost the whole day, and Tom played in front of me with the wooden toys Oliver had made for him. He must have knocked those blocks over a hundred times."

Lois nodded over to the stuffed chair. "Sittin' in his chair was my creature comfort.

"Hitchhiking was his only way to travel to Fort Jackson to enlist. His back was ramrod straight, as he walked up the path to get to Boyce Street. I knew his next steps were to Hart Street and then to Highway 176. His plan was to catch a ride on that main road to Columbia. When the first car slowed down to pick him up, Oliver ran to jump on the running board. There was a loose metal strip on the running board that went slam through the calf of his leg."

With her usual smile on her face, Joanna interrupted, "That man of yo'rn is plenty stubborn, Lois. The blood was running through the bandages when he walked back into the holler. After pullin' the strip out of his laig, he walked to the hospital and stayed jist long enough for stitches. It leaked for might' near a week, 'cause he wouldn't stay off it, like the doctor told him."

"With Buck serving in the US Navy and Ernest in the US Marines, I'm mighty glad Oliver is here," said Fannie.

"Hurt his pride when he finally made it to Fort Jackson after he healed and they wouldn't take him. Said his leg weren't strong enuff for servin'. Don't think I ever seen him so melancholy and quiet, as he was then. Took him awhile to shake it off. God's providence ain't always to our likin'," Lois concluded. "I rightly know that from personal experience."

Amid the trembling windows and distant combat sounds, the Ingle women quietly worked on their quilting rows for a while. Then a new discussion commenced about the new President Harry S. Truman; no one knew much about him.

Sixty-three-year-old President Franklin D. Roosevelt died of a cerebral hemorrhage on April 12, 1945, in Warm Springs, Georgia. Leading America through the Great Depression and the worst days of World War II, FDR was elected four times and served for over twelve years. On Friday, April 13, the Southern Railroad eleven-car funeral train paused in Spartanburg on its journey to Washington, DC.

With their household radios and shared copies of the *Union Daily Times*, bought by Oliver at Kerhulas Newstand, the Ingle clan had no ignorance about local, national, and world news. They loved to read. Either Lois or Oliver read to the boys every night. Once a month, Lois, Tom, and John walked to the Andrew Carnegie Free Library to check out books. *Dr. Doolittle* and *Freckles* were two favorites.

After three hours, the quilting bee ended. Three chairs were dragged back to the kitchen, and Lois rolled the frame back up to the ceiling. Her visitors started back to their own homes.

All their spring gardens were planted on Good Friday. That had been three weeks ago, and weeding was a necessity today. Children had to be rounded up to help with this task. Lois hollered out to her sons to come home.

All the families listened to the *Grand Ole Opry* on Saturday nights, and the women always completed daily chores early so as not to miss it.

As Tom and John crawled around through the vegetable rows pulling the pesky weeds, she headed for the chopping block. Lois needed more kindling for the stove and fireplace. Her arms were strong, and she could swing the ax with one arm. There were plenty of large branches that the boys had dragged to the block for her to cut into kindling.

She took notice of the boys' work and realized that they didn't need quite as much direction as at earlier ages; John was following Tom's lead in most tasks. Unfortunately, this wasn't always good.

Last week, the two of them had left the hollow at dusk to go see the horse ghost. Lois thought they were still at Jenny Belle's playing with Wayne and Bruce. When her sons came running in, shouting for her, with chattering teeth and large eyes, Lois knew she had slipped up. None the worse for their escapade, she listened to their story.

Tom and John wanted to see the horse ghost, so they had walked up to Boyce Street and turned left toward town. They had heard the story of the car that hit a loose horse that had been crossing the road. The car cut the horse in half, and now the rear half of the horse wandered back and forth across the road looking for its head. Both boys were certain they had seen the ghost in the distance.

Lois was glad they were honest about their adventure and relayed that to her sons. But then she also reminded them with a hickory switch about not leaving the holler without permission. Staying behind them to keep them on the straight-and-narrow made for demanding and out-of-the-ordinary days.

Picking up the cut kindling, she knew a light supper was on the menu. It would be cornbread and buttermilk, a favorite for all four of them. If they needed a bite of something sweet, there were some leftover brownies.

Their Saturday night routine was hurried, and the minutes flew by, until it was time for the *Grand Ole Opry.* Oliver had strung a wire clothesline in the backyard. It was also the antenna for the Crosley radio that sat in the kitchen on a table. He ran another wire to the clothesline, and the reception was high-quality. Once, when turning to another station, Oliver picked up a shortwave station in Europe; the unknown language amused everyone.

On Saturday nights, a cast of regulars regaled their listeners on a live radio show. The *Grand Ole Opry* show was divided into thirty-minute segments. Produced at the Ryman Auditorium in Nashville, Tennessee, the music and comedy lasted for four hours. When Uncle Dave Macon, also called the Solemn Old Judge, blew into his brown whiskey jug, then it was time for a new segment. Live commercials for the sponsors of that segment were then sung and narrated; there were no silences.

The Duke of Paducah, Roy Acuff, Minnie Pearl, and Bill Monroe were favorites for Lois and Oliver. Their sons loved the whole show.

The Duke of Paducah and Minnie Pearl were stand-up comics. The Duke had a crazy laugh and ended his routine with "These shoes are killin' me. I'm goin' to the wagon." He often created comic scenarios that he found himself in with his wife.

Minnie Pearl was Lois' favorite; Minnie's contagious "How-DEEE! I'm jes' so proud to be here" always brought smiles to Lois' face. With her signature straw hat and its dangling $1.98 price tag, Minnie was a man-chasing single woman who lived in Grinder's Switch, Tennessee, onstage, but was actually a graduate in theater from Belmont College in Nashville.

"Kissing a man with a beard is a lot like going to a picnic," commented Minnie Pearl one night. "You don't mind going through a little bush to get there."

Every time Lois thought of that line, she laughed. Oliver was clean-shaven, so she was content that it wasn't an issue in their home.

Lois tended to crochet doilies or attach lace to pillow cases while she listened to the radio shows. She gave these as "just because" gifts to her friends and family. When she started working in Cowpens Mill during the summers at age eleven, her mother, Julie, taught her about this small way to cheer people up. Lois had never forgotten. There were many things she longed to pass onto a daughter.

"Papa, when they gonna play that song that made Momma cry?" asked John.

"Oh, that was last week when they played 'Taps,' son. You mind that President Roosevelt died last week? A man named Buddy Harroll played it to say good-bye to our President. Buddy plays with the Pee Wee King's Golden West Cowboys. For certain, it's right sad, but he played it to honor the president's life." Then Oliver sat up straighter in his chair as the host introduced Bill Monroe and the Blue Grass Boys. Monroe was born and raised in Kentucky and had been on the Opry since 1939; he named his group after his home state. He played the mandolin and sang in a high, mournful tenor voice.

As the four-string group composed of a fiddle, guitar, banjo, and mandolin started up with the "Mule Skinner Blues," the boys started clapping and Oliver kept time slapping on his knee. The breakneck speed of the mandolin was spellbinding. When Oliver turned up the volume, the boys started dancing around the table, and Lois put her hands over her ears.

The Opry moved from segment to segment. All four Ingles, finally tired out, went to their bedrooms, crawled in their beds, and continued to listen. Before they all dropped off, the fiddler Arthur Smith and the Cracker Jacks played another favorite, "Mockingbird Hill."

When the sun in the morning peeps over the hill
And kisses the roses 'round my window sill
Then my heart fills with gladness when I hear the trill
Of the birds in the treetops on Mockingbird Hill

Tra la la, tweedle dee dee
It gives me a thrill
To wake up in the morning
To the mockingbird's trill
Tra la la tweedle dee dee
There's peace and good will
You're welcome as the flowers
On Mockingbird Hill

Got a three-cornered plow and an acre to till
And a mule that I bought for a ten-dollar bill
There's a tumble-down shack and a rusty old mill
But it's my Home Sweet Home up on Mockingbird Hill

Tra la la, tweedle dee dee
It gives me a thrill
To wake up in the morning
To the mockingbird's trill
Tra la la tweedle dee dee
There's peace and good will
You're welcome as the flowers
On Mockingbird Hill

When it's late in the evening I climb up the hill
And survey all my kingdom while everything's still
Only me and the sky and an old whippoorwill
Singin' songs in the twilight on Mockingbird Hill

Tra la la, tweedle dee dee.
It gives me a thrill
To wake up in the morning
To the mockingbird's trill
Tra la la tweedle dee dee
There's peace and good will
You're welcome as the flowers
On Mockingbird Hill

"Good night, Tom. Night, John," said Lois softly. "We'll sang agin tomor'."

* * *

Oliver Edward Ingle and Lois Emory married on July 4, 1936. They had four sons: Tom, John, Buck, and Jim.

Born on December 20, 1916, Lois grew up in Cowpens and graduated from Cowpens High School. Starting at age eleven, she worked part time in the Cowpens Mill while she went to school.

After their marriage, she put up ends (reattaching a broken thread) on the spinning frame in the Ottaray Mill in Union. Lois worked second shift, and Oliver was a card grinder on the third shift. This way, one of them was there to look after the children.

When Lois saw a need, either with family or friends, she made sure to help, whatever it took. For our wedding gift, Mom/Lois created a quilt for us; I treasure her work and her memory.

POSSUM FAMILY TREE

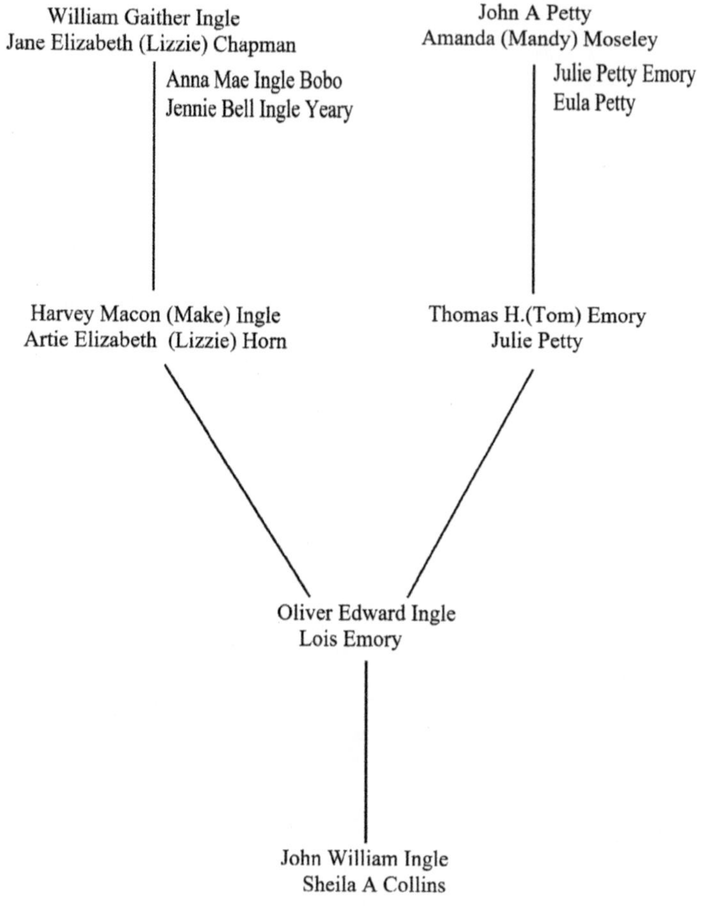
William Gaither Ingle
Jane Elizabeth (Lizzie) Chapman
Anna Mae Ingle Bobo
Jennie Bell Ingle Yeary
John A Petty
Amanda (Mandy) Moseley
Julie Petty Emory
Eula Petty
Harvey Macon (Make) Ingle
Artie Elizabeth (Lizzie) Horn
Thomas H.(Tom) Emory
Julie Petty
Oliver Edward Ingle
Lois Emory
John William Ingle
Sheila A Collins

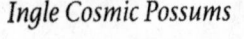

Ingle Cosmic Possums

Left to Right: top row – Betty Ingle, Gwen Moss, Norma Bobo, Sandra Moss, Boyd Ingle, Tom Ingle; Second Row – John Ingle, Sharon Moss, Bruce Yeary (behind), Dennis Moss (holding puppy), Wayne Yeary, Donald Ingle, Talmadge Bobo; Bottom row – unknown (turned around), unknown, unknown, Beth Moss (hand over head), Steve Moss.

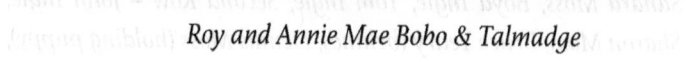

Roy and Annie Mae Bobo & Talmadge

Annie Mae Ingle Bobo

Cling Ingle, Make Ingle with Annie Mae Ingle Bobo

Eula Petty with Lois Emory

Eula Petty

William Gaither & Lizzie Ingle with Fannie

Kyle and Jenny Ingle Yeary

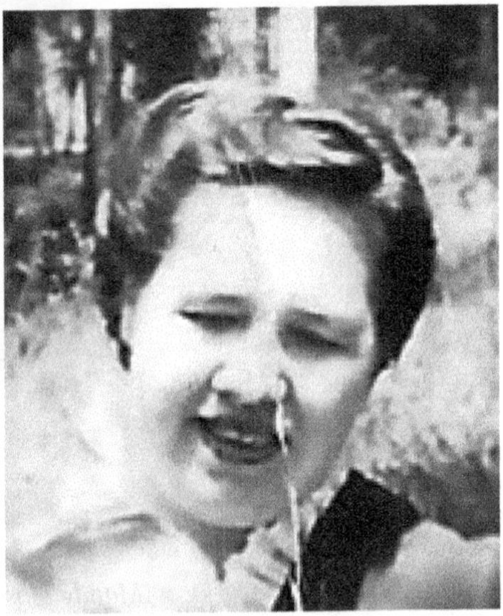

Jenny Yeary

Mandy Moseley

John and Amanda Petty

Julie Petty Emory

Left to right: Top Row - unknown, Tom Emory, Oscar Ingle (Mamie Petty Ingle behind Oscar), Boyd Petty, Second Row – Julie Petty Emory, Judith Ingle (Oscar's daughter), Boyd Ingle (Oscar's son), Ollie Emory Petty (Boyd Petty's wife), Bottom Row – Mandy Petty (Charles' daughter).

Lois Emory at about three or four years

Lois Emory as a teenager

Oliver & Lois Ingle with Make, Tom, and John

Oliver and Lois Ingle

Lizzie Ingle (Make's wife) holding granddaughter Grace Ingle with Audrey

Make and Lizzie Ingle with Theodore, Oscar, and Annie Mae

Make Ingle

MILL HILL RECIPES

Women in the Mill Hill villages depended on their own gardens, chickens, cows, and pigs, as well as buying from the company store for their food. Fruit trees and pecan or walnut trees usually produced bounty to divide with neighbors. They freely shared with each other, and all had a kitchen specialty. Though they had little, the matriarchs made the best of what they had.

They cooked on a wood stove with light from the windows or kerosene lamps. Water was provided from a common well that several families shared. Wooden utensils stirred and turned food heating in cast-iron skillets and bean pots (we still have John's mother's/Lois's), and porcelain pots.

Meals were plain, uncomplicated, and similar. Any leftovers were eaten at the next meal or fed to the animals. Drying and canning vegetables from summer and fall gardens improved winter diets. Nothing was wasted; even watermelon rinds were made into preserves. Though menus were sparse in variety, biscuits or cornbread topped with homemade butter and honey never grew old.

Here are a few well-liked recipes.

SIMPLE SLAW

Choose a solid and firm cabbage from your garden, and squeeze the cabbage head to check to see if it's ready for the table or not. Cut the cabbage off the stem. Wash the cabbage and shake excess water out. Strike the bottom of cabbage down on table to loosen the core. Twist the core to remove. Cut the cabbage to slaw consistency with a very sharp knife. Add salt, pepper, and Duke's mayonnaise to taste. (In 1917, this favorite was created by Mrs. Eugenia Duke at Duke's Sandwich Shop in Greenville, South Carolina.) Stir and serve this extra for Sunday dinner or when company is visiting.

POTATO SALAD

Gather ripe red potatoes, also called new potatoes, from the garden. You might have to sift through the soil to find them under the ground. Wash, but do not peel. Cut into bite size chunks, and boil until semi mushy. (Semi mushy potatoes will liquefy somewhat to leave a lumpy consistency.) Drain and place potatoes in large bowl. Add salt, pepper, and mayonnaise to your liking. Optional additions are relish and garlic salt. Mix well and serve; this is another special dish for company.

PINTO, NAVY, OR ANY DRIED BEANS

Buy a package of dry beans from the company store. Empty the package into a bowl. "Look" the beans over for any bad beans or stones. Place beans in bean pot for cooking. (Most had a dedicated iron pot for beans.) Then add water to at least two fingers over the beans. Add water as needed to keep beans from getting dry as they simmer. Add fatback, about a three-inch piece at least one-inch wide that is partially cut about every thumb width. Either ham bone or bacon can also be used for seasoning. Salt and pepper, and let simmer from 3–4 hours. Serve with cornbread. Many would add mayonnaise or sliced white onions to their beans. ("Beans and taters" or "taters and beans" was the usual daily fare.)

BUTTERMILK AND CORNBREAD FOR SUPPER

Mill Hill people did not eat dinner in the evening. Their main meal of the day was at or around noon, and it was called dinner. The evening meal was supper, usually leftovers or some simple snack—most likely whatever cornbread was left and buttermilk with a piece of sweet onion. Crumble a piece of cornbread left over from dinner/noon meal into a glass of buttermilk. Serve with a spoon for supper. Delicious! (John still enjoys this delicacy.)

FRIED CHICKEN

Fried chicken is an all-time favorite Southern food. There were no KFCs, and families raised their own chickens. The mother would go out to the coop and select a chicken. It seemed that the one she picked would just jump into her hand. She would swing it to wring the neck and then take it to the chopping block to chop its head off. She would then pluck the feathers out and singe it with a burning newspaper or paper sack. Then she cut up the chicken, dipped it in buttermilk, and rolled it in flour. Into the frying pan it went. She fried it until little brown "crispies" covered the bottom. There was never a piece left.

BUTTER AND BUTTERMILK

The cow was milked morning and evening. The morning milk was used mostly for drinking and cooking, but all that was left was put in the crock (a six-gallon stoneware barrel that had a wooden top with a hole that the dasher fit through). The milk was allowed to clabber overnight and churned the next morning. When the milk reached a certain consistency, it yielded up butter. The butter was extracted with a butter pat (a wooden paddle rounded off to the edge). The butter would cling to the paddle and raked off into the butter mold. (We still have Lois' that was handed down to her from her mother Julie and her grandmother Amanda.) The leftover was buttermilk. Buttermilk was used in almost everything that was cooked or baked.

BISCUITS

Biscuits were a staple for breakfast. All mothers made buttermilk biscuits, and there was no acceptable substitute. The flour was kept in the flour bin in the kitchen cabinet; a sifter was attached to the flour bin. On the shelf was the dough bowl. (We have Lois and Julie's dough bowl.) After sifting the flour into the dough bowl and adding lard, Rumford Baking Powder, and buttermilk, she kneaded the dough, patted it into circles, and baked the biscuits. (All of this process was accomplished by eyeing the amounts and guesstimating the timing.) The butter made from the morning's churning was ready with grits and eggs. Of course, eggs were fried in bacon grease. It was just not acceptable to do otherwise. Sometimes there was "run'em down and catch'em" gravy made with a little flour added to the bacon grease and sometimes coffee. If coffee was added, it was called "red-eye" gravy. Breakfast was mouth-watering.

FRIED EGGS

Eggs were a daily staple if you had chickens, and everybody raised chickens, with one setting hen. Bacon was fried first and then the eggs. The eggs always had runny yellows. This was sopped up with the biscuit. A serving of grits was a necessity. It was just not breakfast without, and no respectable mill wife would think of not having grits for breakfast and any other meal if it was reasonable.

FATBACK

Fatback was bought in "slabs" of pork. It was cheap. It was used to season almost everything that needed grease. When frying chicken, two or three strips of fatback were cut and fried in the iron skillet before the chicken. The crispy pieces of fatback were a favorite.

BANANA PUDDING

There was no dessert like 'nanner puddin'. First, the bottom of the bowl was lined with 'niller' wafers and then a layer of banana slices. Another layer of wafers and bananas were added until the cook ran out of one or the other or the bowl got full. The filling was made from the yolks of eggs, sugar, and milk; it was cooked on the stove until thick. This creamy pudding was poured onto the bananas and wafers. The whites were then mixed with sugar and whipped with a fork until frothy and spooned onto the top. It was placed in the oven and baked until the topping was just golden brown. (Fighting over the last bite was always part of eating this dessert!)

REFERENCES

From a Race of Storytellers: Essays on the Ballad Novels of Sharyn McCrumb. 2003. Edited by Kimberley M. Holloway. Macon, GA: Mercer University Press.

Hembree, Michael and David Moore. 1987. *A Place Called Clifton.* Jacobs Press.

Hicks, Jane. 2005. *Blood and Bone Remember: Poems from Appalachia.* Jesse Stuart Foundation Press.

Hicks, Jane. The Cosmic Possum. CosmicPossum.com.

McCrumb, Sharon. 2002. *The Songcatcher.* Signet.

ALSO BY SHEILA INGLE:

Walking with Eliza

Brave Elizabeth

Fearless Martha

Courageous Kate

Eula

"Finding Mister Wright," *Greenville Magazine*

"The Class That Never Was," *The Sandlapper*

For more information about

Sheila Ingle

and

Tales of a Cosmic Possum
please visit:

www.sheilaingle.com
jifamily@charter.net
@SheilaIngle1
www.facebook.com/SheilaIngleAuthor

For more information about
AMBASSADOR INTERNATIONAL
please visit:

www.ambassador-international.com
@AmbassadorIntl
www.facebook.com/AmbassadorIntl